C000157143

THE GOLDEN AGE OF

STEAM LOCOMOTIVE

BUILDING

PHILIP ATKINS

 IN ASSOCIATION WITH THE

THE GOLDEN AGE OF STEAM LOCOMOTIVE BUILDING

PHILIP ATKINS

 IN ASSOCIATION WITH THE NATIONAL RAILWAY

Published by Atlantic Transport Publishers, Trevithick House,
West End, Penryn, Cornwall, TR10 8HE
in association with the National Railway Museum

© Philip Atkins 1999

ISBN: 0 906899 87 7

Design and Layout by Barry C. Lane, Sutton-in-Craven
Reproduction and printing by The Amadeus Press Ltd,
Huddersfield, West Yorkshire

*All rights reserved. No part of this publication may be
reproduced, stored in a retrieval system, or transmitted, in
any form or by any means, electronic, mechanical,
photocopying, recording or o'herwise, without prior
permission in writing from the publishers.*

British Cataloguing in Publication Data
A catalogue record for this book is available from the
British Library

Frontispiece

A general scene enacted in Britain over 100,000 times during the
course of more than a century, but consigned to the history books
only a decade after this photograph was taken, - the assembly of a
new steam locomotive. A British Railways Class 7 mixed traffic
4-6-2 is lowered onto its wheels at Crewe Works in late 1950.

CONTENTS

DEDICATION

This book is dedicated to the author's good friend, Maurice Staton,
who had the good fortune to be raised in a Northern town,
which then still boasted a major railway works and a
leading locomotive builder.

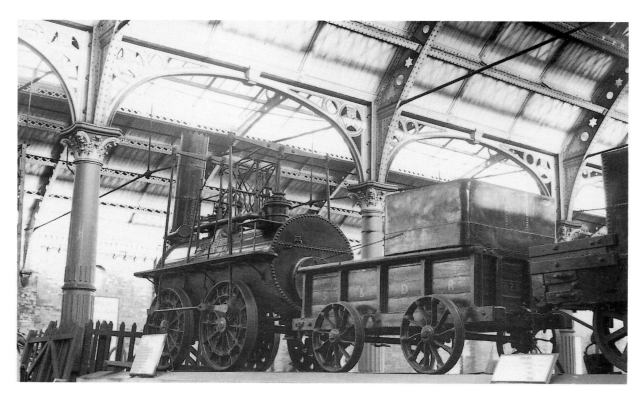

The world's first commercially built steam locomotive, *Locomotion No 1*, delivered by Robert Stephenson & Co to the Stockton & Darlington Railway in September 1825 (RS A1). Photographed in 1954 when as the engine was on display in Darlington Bank Top Station, since 1975 it has been preserved in the Darlington North Road Museum. */G H F Atkins*

INTRODUCTION

The steam locomotive was a British invention which literally changed the world. Approximately 640,000 steam locomotives have been built worldwide, about 110,000 of them in Great Britain. Around 70,000 of these can be attributed to a formally recognisable locomotive industry, which flourished for almost exactly a century, from the mid-1850s until the mid-1950s.

The British locomotive industry was smaller than its counterparts in Germany and the United States. In Germany 155,000 steam locomotives were built, entirely by private industry, comprised of several different enterprises of which the largest was Henschel & Sohn, established in 1848. Slightly more (164,000) were built by American industry, to which should be added 13,000 credited to railroad workshops. After 1900 the American industry was dominated by two manufacturers, the long established Baldwin Locomotive Works (1831) and the recently created American Locomotive Company (Alco) (1901). Around World War 1 both ranked amongst the one hundred largest industrial enterprises in the USA. Their respective maximum annual steam locomotive production figures of 3,580 (1918) and 1,354 (1944) far surpassed that of even the largest British builder, although on several occasions Henschel in Germany achieved an annual production of 1,000 locomotives.

British locomotive production peaked in 1907, fortuitously coinciding with the first *Census of Industrial Production* which helps to place locomotive engineering in context at a time when Great Britain, together with the United States and Germany were the world's leading industrial powers. On this basis at an estimated value of £4.4 million locomotive engineering came a rather poor third after shipbuilding (£48.1 million) and textile machinery (£12.9 million).

The picture is complicated by the fact that a significant proportion of the locomotive valuation is attributable to the activities of British railway workshops, which overall accounted for nearly one third of the steam locomotives built in Great Britain (exports in 1907 were valued at £3.4 million). But for this phenomenon, Britain's locomotive industry would doubtless have

been larger; by 1900 much its production was destined for overseas thanks to Britain's then huge imperial and financial influence worldwide. At that very time, such was the demand that certain British railways were obliged to import locomotives from the United States!

In his excellent study of the American steam locomotive industry, John H White, (then of the Smithsonian Institution) made an astute observation which equally applied to its British counterpart:

> *"It was an industry of extremes, characterised by either too much or too little business activity. Its only consistency was the uneveness of the market and the general over-capacity of the many shops that were almost never called upon to function at their peak level."*

White's study post-dated by seven years the late James Lowe's heroic attempt to catalogue all known British (and Irish) steam locomotive producers. This work inspired the present author to attempt to determine, somewhat laboriously, total annual production figures by railway works and private builders in the United Kingdom, in order to analyse what, if any, pattern might emerge. For example to what extent did total annual production vary from year to year, how did railway works production compare with and relate to private commercial production, and when was the highpoint reached?

All this, coupled with a long term fascination for locomotive production and the establishments involved in it, ultimately led to the writing of this book, which it is hoped will fill a notable gap in the available literature. The writer is indebted to his wife Christine for word processing the manuscript. He would also like to place on record his long friendship with Geoffrey Horsman of Leeds, which effectively began when he first responded to an enquiry from the writer back in 1966! Geoffrey spent his entire working life from 1941 with the Hunslet Engine Company and his knowledge of the workings of the locomotive industry from the inside is well nigh encyclopaedic.

C.P.A., Harrogate, 1998

A general view of the world's largest railway works, Crewe, pictured in July 1895, only a little over fifty years after it was established. By this time Crewe Works had already built some 3,500 steam locomotives, and would be credited with a grand total of 7,331 when production ceased there in December 1958. *NRM/CR A296*

RAILWAY WORKS

At around 34,000 engines, British railway works accounted for nearly one third of national total steam locomotive production and more than 60 per cent of the home railways' requirements over a period of 120 years. This degree of self sufficiency was without parallel overseas, although a comparatively limited number of steam locomotives were also railway built in the United States and Canada, France, and in Australia and New Zealand, but not in Germany.

The practice began in 1841, in England and Ireland almost simultaneously, and was already well established by 1850 when Dr Dionysius Lardner wrote:-

"In the first instance (the railways) derived their supply of (locomotives and rolling stock) from various manufactories of engines and carriages in various parts of the country. The demand, however, for these multiplied with unparalleled rapidity. A supply was required, not only by companies throughout the United Kingdom, but by companies which sprung into existence in all parts of Europe. The established manufacturers were utterly unable to meet demands, so extensive and in a short period all the steam and engine manufacturers in England had more orders than they could satisfy in several years.

Under these circumstances, the railway companies saw themselves reduced to the alternative, either of suspending their progress, or fabricating for themselves. They, of course, adopted the latter measure, and proceeded to erect extensive works for the manufacture of engines and carriages, at convenient points upon the principal lines."

The first of several peaks in locomotive building had indeed occurred in 1840. When addressing the Institution of Civil Engineers in 1852, the eminent Joseph Locke offered a somewhat different explanation.

"At an early period the Grand Junction Railway bought all their locomotives from manufacturers. But these were, necessarily in need of constant repair, and an establishment was formed for that purpose, at Crewe. Then arose the question, whether this establishment could not advantageously be used, not only for the repair, but also for the construction of engines. The plan was tried.........and the cost was found to be much less than the prices which had formerly been paid. Also, the mechanics who repaired the engines saw their defects, and consequently were better able than others to guard against them, in the construction of new ones. These were, evidently, powerful inducements for a company to manufacture their own engines."

The two pre-eminent British railway works, Crewe and Swindon were initiated on then green field sites in the early 1840s and flourished until after the end of the steam era. Other works such as Nine Elms in London, Miles Platting in Manchester, and Gateshead on Tyneside were also established on more circumscribed sites at almost the same time, and were eventually obliged to close down and/or transfer their operations elsewhere. Those works set up in already well established market towns such as Brighton, Derby, Darlington and Doncaster fared rather better. About twenty railway companies had the capability to build their own locomotives by 1870, but it should not be forgotten that the prime function of all of these works was to carry out routine repairs. Even at Crewe, only about 10 per cent of the workforce was occupied in new construction.

Some of the products of the larger works have become legendary, but the achievements of some of the smaller works were remarkable, notwithstanding cramped and difficult circumstances. It is problematical now to gauge to what extent new engines were fabricated at say, Stoke and Maryport, but undoubtedly frames were cut and boilers built there. Castings

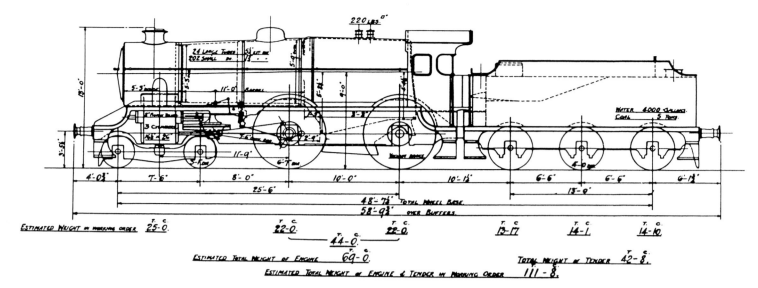

New steam locomotive designs were often initiated in outline diagram form showing estimated weights, for approval by the Civil Engineer who had the undisputed right of veto. Sometimes the end result could differ significantly from the initial proposal, which was often produced by a middle-ranking draughtsman. A notable case was the Southern Railway Class V (or 'Schools') three-cylinder express passenger 4-4-0.

As originally outlined at Waterloo in April 1928 this was to have had a tapered Belpaire boiler, cylindrical smokebox, (possibly) conjugated valve gear for the inside cylinder, and an axleload of 22 tons.

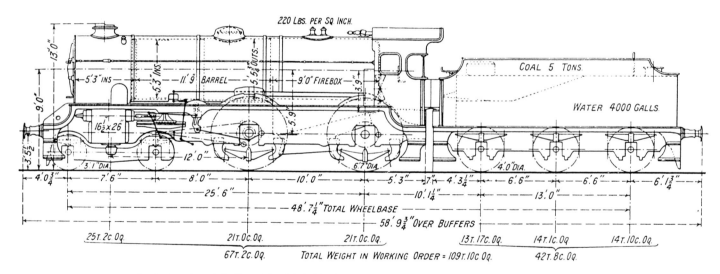

As designed and built at Eastleigh Works in March 1930 the design was distinctly scaled down, ie parallel round-topped boiler, built up smokebox, three independent sets of Walschaerts valve gear, and 21 ton axleload.

were probably made in local foundries, for even Gateshead and Darlington never enjoyed the luxury of a foundry. For many years Darlington obtained its cylinders from Kitson & Co, including the complex monobloc castings for three-cylinder engines such as the elegant Class Z 4-4-2s. Cast steel wheel centres were frequently obtained from such enterprises as Hadfields of Sheffield, or even imported from Belgium.

By the close of the 19th century, the proportion of locomotives built for the home railways by themselves had become very high, and had indeed reached its numerical peak of 626 engines in 1892. Major railway works frequently built locomotives in batches of ten, slotting ten pairs of plate frames simultaneously. The total domestic demand for new locomotives notably slowed down around 1905 and after say 1901, of the major railway

The culmination of the design process, which was not always indulged in for reasons of economy from about 1930 onwards, was the production of an overall general arrangement drawing. This could only be made with reference to numerous subsidiary drawings and was a long and tedious process. One of the last such to be made in Britain was that for the BR Class 7 4-6-2, seen here on the drawing board in Derby Drawing Office c.1950.

companies only the Great Central Railway consistently relied on private industry. Indeed around 1901 - 1903 it put out small pilot orders for 4-4-2s, 4-6-0s, and 0-8-0s, one suspects to get these *designed* in detail as well as built.

By 1914, of the larger companies, only the South Eastern & Chatham Railway had new engines built 'outside' that year. Ironically in the interests of quick delivery ten of these (4-4-0s) were ordered from Messrs Borsig of Berlin as will be related in later. The locomotives had scarcely been delivered when Britain declared war on Germany. On account of the War a curious situation arose on the LNWR in 1915 and later on the GNR. Work had already commenced on batches of 'Prince of Wales' 4-6-0s at Crewe and 2-8-0s at Doncaster, when owing to manpower shortages these were subsequently transferred to the North British Locomotive Company for completion The 'Princes' at least when new bore testimony to having been built in both Crewe and Glasgow, but the NBL plates were quickly removed. In both cases the orders did not include tenders.

The number of railway works actively building steam locomotives steadily declined in the 20th century, from 22 in 1900, to 11 in 1925, and there were only 7 by the end of 1950. These seven remaining works, of which two (Horwich and Brighton) had been restricted to repair work during the 1930s only to be reactivated during World War 2, were collectively responsible, with some assistance from other works, for the 999 British Railways Standard steam locomotives built between 1950 and 1960. These engines were assembled rather than built at a given works owing to a sensible rationalisation policy regarding the manufacture of components. Thus a new Class 5 4-6-0 emerging from Doncaster might have had its cylinders cast at Crewe, which had also flanged the plates for its Darlington-built boiler, and its tender tank fabricated at Ashford.

Although private industry played no direct part in building the BR Standards, because of increasing arrears in the successive building programmes in the early 1950s due to a national steel shortage, quotations were obtained in late 1953 for some of new

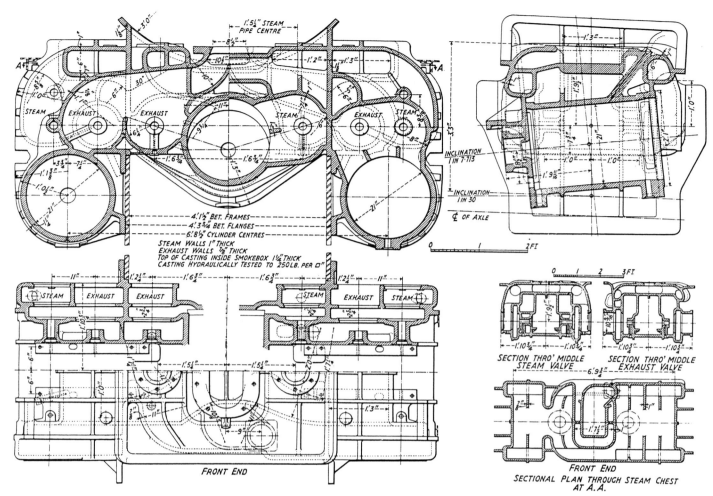

STEAM WALLS 1" THICK
EXHAUST WALLS 7/8" THICK
TOP OF CASTING INSIDE SMOKEBOX 1¼" THICK
CASTING HYDRAULICALLY TESTED TO 250LB. PER □"

FRONT END

SECTION THRO' MIDDLE STEAM VALVE

SECTION THRO' MIDDLE EXHAUST VALVE

FRONT END
SECTIONAL PLAN THROUGH STEAM CHEST AT A.A.

The arrangement drawings showing
the poppet valve steam chests.

One of the most intricate individual
components ever designed for a
British steam locomotive was the
complex 'monobloc' casting
incorporating all three-cylinders for
the Gresley LNER express passenger
2-8-2 No. 2001 *Cock o' the North*,
built at Doncaster Works in 1934.

The newly machined casting as
produced at Gorton Works.
NRM, DON 34/27

The wooden cylinder patterns for a Great Northern Railway three-cylinder 2-6-0 made at Doncaster Works in 1919. These were not simply wooden replicas of the final product, even when allowance had been made for shrinkage on cooling of the casting. In the case of inclined outside cylinders, one pattern could be made to serve for both right and left handed cylinders. *NRM, DON W8*

Class 9F 2-10-0s. North British and Vulcan Foundry each quoted for 35 engines which after deducting 10 per cent profit, etc at £26,718 and £27,335 each respectively was still significantly more than the £23,361 estimated by Crewe Works.

In a later appraisal of its then still very extensive workshop facilities British Railways in early 1959 credited its economy to the following considerations:-

1. The ownership of a large number of workshops permitted the reduction to a minimum of the number of types dealt with at any one works. Similar rationalisation could also be applied to the manufacture of components. Private manufacturers, on the other hand, had to provide for a greater diversity with fewer (usually only one) works.
2. The heavy maintenance commitment of BR workshops demanded the manufacture and holding of large stocks of components, thus providing for greater economy in unit production and purchase.
3. BR workshops did not have to bear charges incurred by contractors in association with profit, advertising and sales.
4. The on-going and over-riding requirement for maintenance helped to smooth the fluctuating demand for new construction (which was in any case a minority activity).

The most expensive single item in producing an entirely new steam locomotive design was, where this was necessary, the production of new press blocks for shaping firebox plates. Here is that as newly made at Crewe Works in July 1950 for the boilers of the new BR Class 7 4-6-2. *NRM, DY 39111*

The foundation of British steam locomotive designs was the main-frame, which was cut or 'slotted' from steel plate 1-1¼ inches thick. Formerly achieved with a band saw, latterly an intensely hot oxygen/coal gas flame was employed moving with respect to a full size wooden profile pattern laid alongside. Here the frames for a new 4-6-2 are being cut at Crewe Works in 1950.   *NRM 2/95*

This was an intriguing echo of Joseph Locke's comments just over a century earlier with respect to Crewe Works. The BR report, produced just before the frames for the final batch of 2-10-0s would have been cut at Swindon Works, effectively refuted the claim sometimes made by the private locomotive industry in the past that the railways' *apparently* lower building costs were lower only because insufficiently high overheads had been ascribed to them. Under normal circumstances the private locomotive industry had indeed long been at a disadvantage with respect to the domestic main line market, particularly after World War 2.

TABLE 1 — Summary of British railway works (which built ten or more locomotives)

Railway (as at 1921)	Works	Period	Number steam locos built	Steam locomotive repairs ceased
London &	Edge Hill (L&MR)	1841-1848	42	—
North Western	Crewe	1843-1958	7331	Dec 1966
	Wolverton	1845-1863	178	—
	Longsight	1854-1858	16	—
London &	Nine Elms	1843-1908	815	1910
South Western	Eastleigh	1910-1950	320	Oct 1965
North British	Cowlairs	1844-1924	900	Sept 1966
	St Margarets	1856-1869	39	—
Great Western	Swindon	1846-1960	5964	Feb 1965
	Wolverhampton	1859-1906	794	Feb 1964
	Bristol (B&ER)	1859-1876	35	—
Caledonian	Greenock	1846-1855	97	—
	St Rollox	1854-1928	1000	1962
Lancashire &	Miles Platting	1847-1881	522	—
Yorkshire	Bury (East Lancs)	1862-1877	16	—
	Horwich	1889-1957	1840	May 1964
North Eastern	Gateshead	1849-1910	1023	1959
	York	1854-1884	13	1905
	Darlington	1864-1957	2269	Jan 1966
Midland	Derby	1851-1957	2995	Sept 1963
Great Eastern	Stratford	1851-1924	1702	May 1960
London, Brighton & South Coast	Brighton	1852-1957	1211	mid-1958
South Eastern &	Ashford (SER)	1853-1944	790	mid-1962
Chatham	Longhedge (LC&DR)	1869-1904	54	1911
Taff Vale	Cardiff	1856-1897	84	1926
Glasgow & South Western	Kilmarnock	1857-1921	392	1952
Maryport & Carlisle	Maryport	1857-1900	33	1924
Great Central	Gorton	1858-1949	1006	April 1963
	Sheffield	1874-1880	12	—
North London	Bow	1863-1906	163	1957
Great Northern	Doncaster	1867-1957	2224	Nov 1963
North Staffordshire	Stoke	1868-1923	197	c.1927
Highland	Inverness	1869-1906	41	July 1959
Midland & Great Northern Joint	Melton Constable	1897-1910	12	c.1936
Great North of Scotland	Inverurie	1909-1921	10	late 1965

These figures are taken from *British Steam Locomotive Builders* (Lowe, 1975).

The heart of a locomotive was its boiler, for decades manufactured under conditions which would not be countenanced in more recent times by health and safety legislation. Prior to the ear-splitting rivetting process, pre-drilled holes in the overlapping barrel courses had to be lined up and 'reamed' (ie smoothed out). Here an upturned 4-6-2 boiler is under construction at Doncaster Works in 1947. *NRM, DON 47/179*

TABLE 2 — Estimated Total Annual Steam Locomotive Production by British Railway Works 1841-1960 () indicates 5ft 3in gauge engines built by Crewe and Derby Works for Irish subsidiaries (except 1918, by Gorton for Railway Operating Division)

1841	4	1871	358	1901	441	1931	345
1842	10	1872	393	1902	477	1932	268
1843	9	1873	397	1903	456	1933	215(+4)
1844	16	1874	430	1904	417	1934	298
1845	27	1875	426(+2)	1905	413(+4)	1935	355
1846	59	1876	312	1906	477	1936	331
1847	93	1877	351	1907	513	1937	369
1848	108	1878	331	1908	391(+2)	1938	287
1849	63	1879	348	1909	369	1939	276
1850	45	1880	385	1910	358	1940	146
1851	46	1881	342	1911	319	1941	139
1852	70	1882	352	1912	347	1942	223
1853	90	1883	391	1913	366	1943	158
1854	154	1884	402	1914	335(+2)	1944	253
1855	119	1885	345	1915	131	1945	261
1856	99	1886	322	1916	148	1946	244(+4)
1857	114	1887	375	1917	187	1947	286(+6)
1858	91	1888	378	1918	201(+3)	1948	299
1859	137	1889	411	1919	249	1949	231(+4)
1860	165	1890	548	1920	289	1950	284(+4)
1861	210	1891	609	1921	311	1951	235
1862	183	1892	626	1922	168(+2)	1952	154
1863	268	1893	487	1923	225(+3)	1953	140
1864	248	1894	509	1924	272	1954	190
1865	227	1895	507	1925	335	1955	156
1866	306	1896	577	1926	312	1956	129
1867	302	1897	595	1927	339	1957	141
1868	307	1898	596(+1)	1928	361	1958	62
1869	261	1899	607	1929	412	1959	15
1870	275	1900	589	1930	305	1960	3

Darlington Works Erecting Shop in 1910 showing two powerful NER Class Y three-cylinder 4-6-2T goods tank engines under construction. The frames for further engines can also be seen laid out or already set up. *NRM 337/83*

The massively robust mainframes are set up, 13 September 1919.
NRM, DY 11157

The basic stages in steam locomotive construction are neatly encapsulated in a series of dated negatives which recorded the construction of the unique Midland Railway four-cylinder 0-10-0 at Derby Works in late 1919. Specifically designed for banking passenger and freight trains up the 1 in 38 incline out of Bromsgrove, construction had actually commenced in the summer of 1914, but was almost immediately postponed for five years because of international events. Construction resumed in earnest during the latter half of 1919, and the engine made its trial trip on New Year's Day, 1920.

Just over one week later the two cylinder castings, each incorporating two cylinders which shared a common steam chest, have been mounted. The threads which line up the centres of the outside cylinder barrels with the driving axle centre can be seen, 22 September, 1919.
NRM, DY 11160

One month later the boiler, which was the largest ever made at Derby Works, has been mounted. (Construction had been suspended for several days by a national rail strike). 2 October 1919.

NRM, DY 11164

The engine is now virtually complete, standing on its own wheels, and with connecting, coupling rods, and valve gear set up. It is attired in grey primer, and united with its tender it will sit for its formal portrait three weeks later. 27 November 1919.

NRM, DY 11170

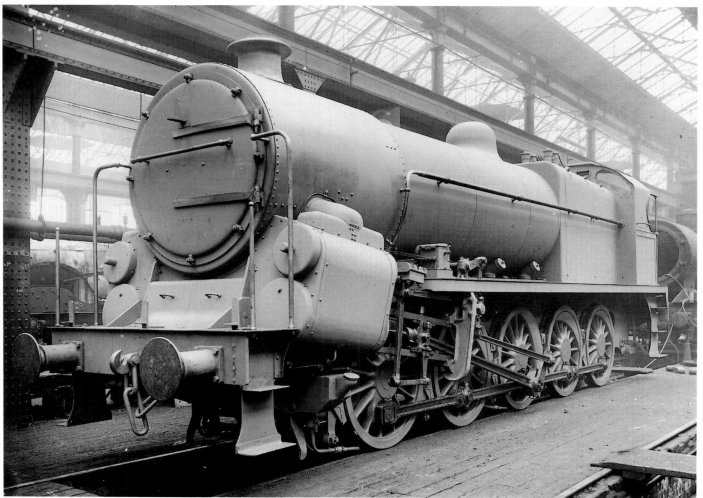

During the closing months of new steam locomotive construction at Horwich Works in 1957, a British Railways Standard Class 4 2-6-0 and its tender (both fully painted) stand in the Erecting Shop. Horwich Works, which commenced operations in 1889 and was the last *major* entirely new British railway works to be established. (Eastleigh Locomotive Works, opened in 1910, was built adjacent to the already existing LSWR carriage shops and its total production, although including 4-6-2s, was only modest by comparison).

NRM, HOR 37/17

A 4-4-0 locomotive for India, built by the Vulcan Foundry, being embarked in partly dismantled form at Birkenhead Docks, c.1880. For several decades early British-built steam locomotives were transported across the world by sailing ships. *NRM*

THE WORKSHOP OF THE WORLD
1830–1897

A nation's (steam) locomotive production was for many years a fair measure of its industrial muscle. In this, as in many other fields, Great Britain led the world for the greater part of the nineteenth century when it was popularly called the 'Workshop of the World'. British-built locomotives were the first to appear in at least twenty countries in six continents (see Table 5).

Only twenty years after Richard Trevithick had created the first steam locomotive, Robert Stephenson & Co set up the world's first locomotive factory at Forth Street, Newcastle-upon-Tyne in 1823. However for about thirty years steam locomotives were built in Britain by a myriad of general manufacturers which came and went, often leaving little record of their activities. By about 1860 a second generation of more specifically oriented en-

terprises was beginning to emerge, which included a new sub-culture, the builder of locomotives for purely industrial purposes, which particularly became associated with a certain district of Leeds. Two expatriate Germans, Charles Beyer and Henry Dübs, played a leading part in what could by then be termed the British locomotive industry. Perhaps by way of compensation two Englishmen, John Haswell and John Cockerill, established locomotive building enterprises in continental Europe, in Austria and Belgium respectively, the latter as early as 1835.

The steam locomotive could not have been invented any earlier than it was, its development initially being constrained by the materials and technology available. Rapid advances in steel production after c.1870 had profound repercussions.

A large Manchester-built 'Sharpie' 2-2-2 built in 1847 for the 5ft 3in gauge Great Southern & Western Railway in Ireland.

Locomotive manufacture in Britain was initially very much a haphazard affair, sometimes involving enterprises which dated back to the horse dominated 18th century, iron founders, machine tool and general machinery manufacturers. There was no precedent for locomotive building, the closest in terms of precision engineering would have been textile machinery production. Many early builders of locomotives only produced a small number of these. Of fifteen enterprises established before say 1845, which subsequently produced one hundred or more engines,

half of them had ceased production by 1865. By 1860 those builders which (then unknowingly) were destined to survive into the then still distant 20th century, had already effectively seen off the opposition, and they were joined by two new enterprises established by the Germans referred to earlier.

TABLE 3 — British locomotive manufacturers* established before 1845 which produced at least 100 locomotives (*name given is not necessarily the original carried by the firm)

Builder	Location	Established	Locomotive Production
R Stephenson & Co	Newcastle	1823	1825 - (1958)
E Bury	Liverpool	c.1823	1830 - 1850†
R & W Hawthorn Ltd	Newcastle	1817	1831 - (1958)
E B Wilson & Co	Leeds	1831	1831 - 1859†
Rothwell, Hick & Rothwell	Bolton	c.1830	1831 - 1864†
Vulcan Foundry	Nr Warrington	1830	1833 - (1956)
Sharp Stewart & Co	Manchester	1828	1833 - (1958)
Haigh Foundry	Wigan	1810	1836 - 1856†
R B Longridge & Co	Bedlington	1785	1837 - 1852†
Jones & Potts	Nr Warrington	1837	1837 - 1860†
Nasmyth Wilson & Co	Manchester	1836	1838 - (1939)
William Fairbairn & Co	Manchester	1816	1839 - 1863†
Slaughter & Co	Bristol	1837	1841 - (1935†)
Neilson & Co	Glasgow	c.1837	1843 - (1958)

† ceased production

The demand for locomotives, both at home and abroad, rapidly increased during the late 1830s and attained its first peak in 1840. Demand exceeding supply was one factor in the trend for British railway companies to build their own locomotives from the 1840s onwards. A very sharp drop in investment resulted in few new locomotives being built in 1843, as compared to the recent 1840 peak, but demand later picked up again with the 'Railway Mania' period of 1844-46. At this stage no commercial builder of locomotives strictly confined itself purely to locomotive building, which was a trend which began to emerge in the 1850s, most notably with the establishment of Beyer, Peacock & Co in Manchester in 1854. Shortly afterwards one of the most prominent early builders, E B Wilson & Co of Leeds, passed *out*

An exactly contemporaneous Bury 2-2-2 for the GS & WR, now preserved at Cork.   *J G Click Collection, NRM (JGC I/47)* of business. During this early phase the stock in trade of the British builders was the 2-2-2 in its various forms, 'Patentees' from Newcastle, 'Sharpies' from Manchester, and 'Jenny Linds' from Leeds. About 500 'Sharpies' alone were built.

From around 1860 several new enterprises were in the ascendant, including the new genre which tended to specialise in the production of locomotives for purely industrial purposes. Thus a period of only six years witnessed the emergence of four such builders, ie Manning Wardle Ltd (1858), Andrew Barclay Sons & Co Ltd (1859), Hudswell Clarke & Co (1860) and the Hunslet Engine Co (1864). With the exception of Barclay's in Kilmarnock, first established as general engineers in 1817, the other three were entirely new and what is more they even occupied adjacent premises in the Hunslet district of Leeds, where two other locomotive builders, Kitson's and Fowler's, would also be found.

These 'small' locomotive builders soon built locomotives for export, and to a limited extent for the smaller home railways, especially in South Wales which never aspired to building their own locomotives (with the exception of the Taff Vale Railway during the 19th century). Such lines along with such English enterprises as the Furness, Hull & Barnsley, and Midland & South Western Junction railways ultimately become the most consistent domestic customers of the private locomotive builders as a whole, but their requirements were only modest.

An attractive R Stephenson & Co 2-4-0, No 17 *Caroline* built in 1861 for the Danish State Railways, restored and in steam in 1954. The Sandinavian countries have a remarkably fine collection of mid-19th century British-built locomotives, Sweden in particular having several early Beyer, Peacock engines with no parallel in Britain.

P Ransome Wallis Collection, NRM (PRW 617)

TABLE 4 — Estimated Annual Production of Early Leading British Locomotive Manufacturers, 1831 - 1860

	Major*	EB	EBW	RHR	HF	JP	RBL	WF	SI	Total
1831	16	1	2	1						20
1832	27	4	2	4						37
1833	43	5	1	0						49
1834	26	8	2	2						38
1835	28	11	1	2						42
1836	44	9	5	1	3					62
1837	47	8	3	19	8	2	1			88
1838	111	13	6	18	10	9	4			171
1839	155	26	10	7	8	17	21	8		252
1840	167	41	25	4	7	22	11	2		279
1841	132	35	11	12	10	8	11	3	11	233
1842	108	18	10	6	1	8	4	7	1	165
1843	111	7	0	0	2	2	0	3	0	125
1844	100	7	0	0	10	2	0	0	9	128
1845	200	26	0	2	0	39	13	0	12	292
1846	254	37	29	18	0	61	31	7	27	464
1847	**277**	57	35	23	**13**	40	**42**	22	19	**528**
1848	277	42	41	0	3	40	14	35	13	465
1849	199	42	13	0	4	5	20	31	21	335
1850	89	1	36	4	4	0	0	17	1	152
1851	116	†	37	5	6	0	21	7	4	196
1852	161		25	0	4	1	13	14	9	227
1853	174		45	3	1	7	†	32	23	285
1854	225		65	7	1	8		34	18	358
1855	239		54	11	2	8		**44**	16	374
1856	161		56	0	6	6		27	9	265
1857	118		44	27	†	3		36	2	230
1858	211		8	6		2		8	2	237
1859	226		2	2		0		24	20	274
1860	248		†	2		4		17	14	285

* see Appendix 6   † ceased production

Official works portrait of 5ft 6in gauge 0-8-0 for Spain built by Sharp Stewart & Co in 1878.

An engine of the same batch seen still in service at Tarragona in 1962. All thirteen locomotives built 1878-1880 for the Tarragona Barcelona Railway were still in RENFE stock in
1963, of which two still remained as late as 1967. An example has been preserved.
P Ransome Wallis Collection, NRM (PRW 5709)

If one analyses the widely fluctuating estimated total annual new build for the British main line railways one finds an underlying trend whereby annual requirement increased by almost ten engines per year until reaching a peak in 1895, thereafter *decreasing* by almost exactly the same amount. Overall this increase was met by the output of railway works leaving an average balance of about 160 engines per year to be met by private industry. As the latter's production in itself increased steadily this represented a decreasing proportion of its output. The salvation of the British locomotive industry was to be its extensive export market, which was facilitated by the rapidly expanding British colonial and financial empires which stretched across the globe. These in turn were serviced by a huge mercantile shipping industry.

Many British locomotives were exported in the 1830s, but their numbers would initially decrease in the 1840s as several leading European countries commenced indigenous production. However, the second export era effectively began around 1852 when the first locomotives were despatched to India, which would subsequently absorb almost 25 per cent of the combined production of the major British builders over the course of the next hundred years. Other significant markets would be Australia, Southern Africa, South America, and for a period, Japan, but not China.

Manchester was the pre-eminent locomotive building centre in Britain, and therefore the world, in the 1870s. However in the mid-1880s its longest established builder, Sharp Stewart & Co removed to Glasgow thereby significantly boosting the fortunes of Scotland's second city by setting up in direct competition with Neilson & Co and Dübs & Co there.

Locomotive exports showed a steady increase throughout the 19th century, curiously being particularly strong during 1883 - 85 when the UK domestic economy was notably depressed. The actual peak in British locomotive exports was reached in 1907 and in *absolute* terms, the 'golden years' were 1902 - 1914 when exports consistently exceeded 600 engines per annum, even approaching 1,000 in 1907. The sheer diversity was bewildering.

Ten years before, the year 1897 had been a watershed in British history, the Diamond Jubilee of Queen Victoria, and the high noon of British Imperialism. However, for half of that year a large proportion of British manufacturing industry was at a standstill. Steel production in the United States had overtaken that in Britain in 1891 as had that in Germany only three years later. By 1913 US steel production was nearly four times, and German steel output almost twice British. By the closing years of the 19th century Great Britain, still great in the imperial sense, was no longer the 'Workshop of the World' it once had been.

TABLE 5 — The First Locomotives in Overseas Countries to be Supplied by British Locomotive Builders 1828 - 1871

Year	Country	Type	Builder	Works No
1828	United States	0-4-0	R Stephenson	RS/A12
1834	Ireland	2-2-0	Sharp	S/D
1834	Russia	?	R Stephenson	RS/93
1835	Belgium	2-2-2	R Stephenson	RS/88
1835	Germany*	2-2-2	R Stephenson	RS/118
1836	Austria	2-2-0	R Stephenson	RS/128
1836	Canada	0-4-0	R Stephenson	RS/127
1837	France	0-4-2	R Stephenson	RS/154
1839	Italy	2-2-2	R B Longridge	RBL/108
1839	Holland	2-2-2	R B Longridge	RBL/119
1846	Denmark	2-2-2	Sharp	S/364
1848	Spain	2-2-2	Jones & Potts	JP/
1851	Norway	2-4-0	R Stephenson	RS/815
1851	Brazil	2-2-2WT	W Fairbairn	WF/L
1852	India	2-4-0 ·	Vulcan Foundry	VF/324
1852	Egypt	2-4-0	R Stephenson	RS/822
1854	Australia*	2-4-0	R Stephenson	RS/954
1856	Argentina	2-2-0ST	E B Wilson	EBW/570
1856	Sweden	2-4-0	Beyer, Peacock	BP/31
1857	Portugal	2-4-0WT	E B Wilson	EBW/572
1859	South Africa	0-4-2	Hawthorn(Leith)	H/162
1859	Turkey	4-4-0	R Stephenson	RS/1201
1860	Finland	4-4-0	Brassey	B/80
1863	New Zealand*	2-4-0T	Slaughter	SI/488
1871	Japan	2-4-0T	Vulcan Foundry	VF/614

* Strictly speaking the first British built locomotives in Australia and New Zealand were preceded by locally built locomotives in 1854 and 1861 respectively.

3

THE LOCOMOTIVE FAMINE
1898–1900

1899

Durii:g 1899 the trade of the world augmented rapidly. Each month was better than the month which preceded it. In a way, and to an extent never before approached, the demand for manufactured articles developed day by day....Nor is there at the moment the smallest symptom of a falling off in demand.

The Engineer, 5 January 1900

Such was Britain's industrial pre-eminence that during the course of nearly sixty years only two British railways resorted to builders overseas for locomotives. Between 1839 and 1842 the Birmingham & Gloucester Railway obtained seventeen 4-2-0s from Norris of Philadelphia, while in 1865 the Great Eastern ordered fifteen 2-2-2s and 2-4-0s from the leading French manufacturer, Schneider of Le Creusot. Then, as the 19th century drew to its close, during 1898 - 99 *six* British railway companies ordered a total of 93 engines from overseas.

This unusual situation arose through a unique combination of circumstances. An unpredictable very rapid increase in trade, and therefore in the demand for locomotives, followed hard on the heels of a general engineering strike which had effectively closed down several British locomotive builders for six months, thereby throwing their order books badly into arrears.

The demand for locomotives seemed to follow a 7 - 8 year cycle, the previous peak having occurred around 1892, which was followed in 1893 by a major coal strike which hit the railways and industry badly. By 1896 there were distinct signs of an upturn, but there was a general engineering strike involving over 100,000 men in many branches of manufacturing industry between July 1897 and January 1898. Hitherto, depending upoii circumstances, locomotives ordered early in a new year could often be hard at work before that year had ended. Now the manufacturers were forced to concede deliveries of up to two years.

One of the first British railways to discover this was the soon to be opened narrow gauge Lynton & Barnstaple Railway in North Devon, which had obtained three 2-6-2Ts from Manning Wardle Ltd of Leeds in 1897. In early 1898 it calculated that a fourth engine was required, but no British builder could offer early delivery. In April 1898 a 2-4-2T was ordered from the Baldwin Locomotive Works in Philadelphia, where it was built only the following month. It was delivered, assembled, and running before the end of July 1898.

A serious situation was rapidly developing on some of the largest British railways, even though they regularly built their own locomotives. Particularly critical was the Midland which also regularly resorted to contractors. As of the end of 1897 it had 170 new engines ordered from 'outside', delivery of which should have commenced in mid-1898, but as that year drew to a close not one was yet in prospect. The Company came under particular fire from Sheffield industrialists on account of its apparent inability to move steadily accumulating stockpiles of coal from the pithead to where it was required in rapidly increasing quantities.

Shortly before Christmas 1898, the Midland Railway announced that it had ordered twenty 2-6-0s from the United States, ten each from the Baldwin and Schenectady Locomotive Works.

The MR Chairman, Sir Ernest Paget, defended this by stating 'we should very much have preferred homemade goods, whether they be engines or anything else. The question of cost did not enter our calculations.' He pointed out that during 1898 total train mileage on the Midland had increased by more than two million miles, and that at a given time 90 per cent of its engines were in steam, rather than a preferred 75 per cent.

The Baldwin order was subsequently increased to thirty engines, which had to be erected at Derby in the open air (it was fortunately an exceptionally fine summer) by supervised unskilled labour, which in itself had been difficult to recruit owing to the booming economy and consequent high levels of employment.

In early 1899 the Great Northern and Great Central railways

Ten imported Baldwin 2-6-0s under assembly in the open air outside Derby Works during the fortuitously fine summer of 1899.

NRM 266/83

each ordered twenty very similar engines from Baldwins, most of which arrived during 1900. However, the last of the GNR engines was sent by the builders to the Paris Exhibition of that year, where it was studiously ignored by one *Railway Magazine* correspondent. However, another had earlier observed 'it is pleasing to observe the design follows most closely on British lines', which it patently did not. On the other hand the Schenectady 2-6-0s *were* comparatively anglicised in appearance. The Baldwin 2-6-0s in general were elsewhere variously described as 'uncouth, assemblages of iron', and for 'Mogul read mongrel'.

On inspecting the Baldwin 2-6-0s under erection at Derby the leading commentator of the day, Charles Rous Marten, was not unduly critical of them and their 'alien' characteristics, perhaps because Baldwin locomotives were rapidly becoming well established in his native New Zealand. He was escorted by Samuel Johnson, the MR Locomotive Superintendent, who reserved his judgement but later revealed that the American engines proved to be heavier on fuel, lubricants and repairs than the traditional British inside-cylinder 0-6-0s.

Of late the dramatically increasing annual locomotive production figures of the Baldwin Locomotive Works had regularly featured in *The Engineer*, which in its editorial for 7 April 1899 offered a remarkably even-handed analysis of the controversial situation. Firstly it did not accuse the British railways of a lack of foresight. 'Traffic has augmented in a way that was not anticipated. Trade has undergone an enormous development within the last few months. Directors saw nothing twelve months ago to justify the giving out of large orders for engines, and they would have been censured had they bought locomotives for which there was no necessity.'

The Engineer also questioned the necessity on the part of British builders to provide locomotives which were 'too good and too perfect for the work they had to perform' on colonial and overseas railways, upon which operating conditions were more harsh than at home where the permanent way was laid with heavier rail to a higher standard. It criticised consulting civil engineers in London for laying down unnecessarily elaborate locomotive design standards with which British builders were obliged to comply, unlike their American competitors. American engines with their more rugged design and compensated suspension were better suited to most foreign climes, but wore out more quickly.

Indeed, none of the eighty 2-6-0s in Britain would last above sixteen years, but the products of a *third* American builder, would last rather longer. Late in 1899 the Cooke Locomotive & Machine Works of Paterson, New Jersey supplied two 0-8-2Ts to the Port Talbot Railway, and five 0-6-2Ts to the Barry Railway, all with bar frames and outside cylinders. The Barry Company stated that the American firm had quoted a price of £1,800 per engine as against £2,800 by a British builder, for an equivalent engine, and nine months earlier delivery.

The Barry Railway also ordered five inside-cylinder 0-6-2Ts from SA Franco-Belge of Liege, in Belgium, the last of which was sent for display at the 1900 Paris Exhibition.

Overseas locomotive manufacturers clearly capitalised on the British builders' discomfiture, but the latter wasted no time once the engineering strike had ended in attempting to regain lost ground. The largest, Neilson's, for instance, resorted to day and night shifts, but major orders from Russia and China were lost to American builders.

As far as the home railways were concerned an unprecedented all but *two thousand* new locomotives were put into traffic during 1899 - 1900, about 650 of them 0-6-0 goods engines.

The Locomotive Magazine for May 1899 reported that 'the English companies appear to be suffering at the present time from a great scarcity of locomotives.' The next month it recounted 'the demand for goods engines still continues unabated, nearly all companies being urgently in need of more, but the Great Central especially so. On the last named railway some fifty trains daily are now being worked by engines of the Great Eastern, Great Northern, Lancashire & Yorkshire, and North Eastern Companies.' (Remarkably the newly styled GCR did not put a single new 0-6-0 goods engine into traffic between mid-1897 and early 1901).

It was not only the 'English Companies'; in Glasgow all three builders and the Caledonian Railway's own St Rollox Works were almost simultaneously between them turning out 79 0-6-0s of J F McIntosh's new '812' class.

The *fin de siècle* demand for new locomotives was remarkably sustained and was still going strong in late 1900 nearly three years after it had begun. The largest British builder, Neilson, Reid & Co, logged orders for a total of *one hundred* 0-6-0 goods engines from the Midland and Great Central railways on a single day, Wednesday 19 October, just one week after receiving their respective specifications.

A strong flavour of those heady times, not to say the manner in which business was then transacted, comes down to us in transcripts of telegrams ('wires') and letters which passed between Oliver Holt, Secretary to the Great Central Railway in Manchester, and Hugh Reid, Managing Director of Neilsons' in Glasgow, between 15 and 24 October 1900.

On 15 October, Neilson's had responded to an enquiry from the GCR for 75 0-6-0s of new design, quoting £3,345 per engine, with delivery to commence nine months after receipt of complete working drawings, and continuing at a rate of eight engines per month.

The GCR replied on 18 October by awarding an order for forty engines only at £3,345 each under penalty. This was acknowledged the following day by Neilson's, who, despite the reduced order, now confirmed a delivery rate of only *four* engines

INSTRUCTIONS FOR TENDERING.

The Tenders must be sent in on the attached form, addressed to the Secretary of the Locomotive Committee, Midland Railway, Derby, so as to be received by him not later than 9.0 a.m. on Thursday, the 18th October, 1900.

The Directors do not bind themselves to accept the lowest or any Tender.

SAMUEL W. JOHNSON,
Locomotive Superintendent.

Derby, Oct. 10th, 1900.

The Midland Railway's requirement for goods engines was still well nigh insatiable over one year later, as is evident from this extract from an 0-6-0 specification which allowed potential builders barely one week in which to respond.

CONTRASTS 1

A Johnson Midland Railway Class 2 0-6-0 No. 2268 built by Sharp Stewart & Co in 1897, of the ultimate 'M' variety of which large numbers were built during 1900-02.

NRM, F Burtt Collection, FB 745

The American alternative, Baldwin 2-6-0, MR No 2526, early in its short career, at Lancaster Green Ayre shed, early 1900s.

NRM, S P Higgins collection (SPM/MID/10)

Robinson Great Central Railway Class 9J 0-6-0, No 982, built by
Neilson, Reid & Co in late 1901, brand new at Neasden.

NRM F Burtt Collection, FB 605

CONTRASTS 2

Baldwin 2-6-0 GCR No 960. The Baldwin 2-6-0's built for the
MR, GCR, and GNR during 1899-1900 were very similar but not
quite identical, particularly as regards the balance weights.

per month, while still agreeing to a penalty of £50 per engine per month.

Holt then wired Neilson's on 20 October:

"Thanks letter. Mr Reid agreed with me to amend Tender and apply £3,345 all round and conditions must be eight Engines and Tenders per month in accordance with this agreement."

Reid replied at some length by letter the same day.

Dear Sir

As we close at 12-o'clock on Saturdays your telegram has not received a wire reply.

I certainly agreed to amend our offer to the extent of taking either the 45 or 30 Goods Engines at £3,345 each, but this was for acceptance by wire before noon on the following day (Wednesday) as I told you we had to fix our tender for the Midland Railway Engines then. My brother left Glasgow by the 1.30 pm train on Wednesday for Derby, and before he left (after waiting in vain for your expected wire) we fixed the prices and delivery for the Midland Engines and it was not till late in the afternoon that your wire making a counter offer arrived here.

The Midland Company asked quotations for 40 Goods Engines and Tenders, and 30 Tank Engines, and our offer of delivery to them was at the rate of 4 engines per month.

The Midland Directors on Thursday afternoon placed 60 Goods Engines and Tenders with us, thus we got 60 Engines instead of 40 asked for at the price originally quoted, and with delivery of the additional 20 to follow on after completion of the 40 without penalty clause.

Whatever, therefore, we might have been able to do before we tendered for the Midland Company's Engines, we might not be able to do afterwards, and I went specially up to Manchester to point this out to you and Mr Robinson (the GCR Locomotive Superintendent).

From what I have said you will see that you really are getting even better terms from us than the Midland as they accepted our original quotation for 40 engines and gave us another 20 to follow on without deduction in price, while you asked our price for 45 and gave us 40 only at the moderate prices we originally quoted for 75.

If you are satisfied with the explanation I have endeavoured to give and are prepared to accept delivery of the Engines at the rate of four per month, you might kindly wire us on Monday, withdrawing your telegram of today.
Yours very truly
Hugh Reid

A flurry of telegrams then passed between Manchester and Glasgow on 22 October. Holt initially suggested that the agreed rate of delivery be reduced to six engines per month, which Reid immediately replied was not possible and suggested cancellation of the order altogether if four per month was not acceptable.
Holt responded:

"Disappointed you cannot meet us, but in the absence of my Chairman (1) will take responsibility of confirming order delivery to be four per month."

In the event, Neilson's delivered the forty 0-6-0s to the Great Central Railway between September 1901 and May 1902, and the sixty engines to the Midland between June 1901 and September 1902 (the final five going to the Somerset & Dorset Joint Railway).

By 1901 the pace was noticeably slackening, with total train mileage that year slightly down on that for 1900. In Great Britain both total train mileage and total (reported) locomotive stock had more than tripled between 1860 and 1900. Total *freight* train mileage actually peaked at 175 million in 1900 before declining, but total *passenger* train mileage continued to increase until 1911 (to 258 million). The result was a plateau of nearly 400 million total train miles for several years after 1900, and in 1905 for the first time more locomotives were broken up than were built. In the new century the demand for new locomotives greatly decreased and except for the minor railways this largely fell within the capacity of the railways' own workshops. Overseas markets were also diminishing, either through foreign competition, particularly from the United States and Germany, or increasing self sufficiency on the part of the countries themselves. Fortunately for the British locomotive industry this would never be the case in Africa or South America, but it would eventually come to pass in India with the industry's own assistance.

TABLE 6 — British Total Train Mileage and Locomotive Stock Changes 1895 - 1905

Year	Total train mileage (million)	Change	Reported total loco stock*	Change	New locos to traffic†
1895	323	+6	17,871	+307	615
1896	339	+16	18,159	+288	738
1897	351	+12	18,675	+516	808
1898	364	+14	19,005	+330	699
1899	379	+15	19,624	+619	1005
1900	385	+6	20,325	+701	990
1901	382	-3	20,811	+486	703
1902	382	0	21,220	+409	628
1903	371	-11	21,445	+225	561
1904	373	+2	21,586	+141	636
1905	378	+5	21,280	-306	462

* Reported locomotive stock prior to 1913 was Capital Stock. Total locomotive stock included Duplicate stock and was typically about 5 per cent greater.
† estimated

One of the most impressive locomotive classes to be built by a private builder for a British main line railway was the majestic 4-6-4T for the Glasgow & South Western Railway, of which six were delivered by the North British Locomotive Company in 1922. Designed in outline only in the Kilmarnock drawing office, the working drawings were produced by the builder, and the engines cost £16,125 apiece. G & SWR No 541 poses brand new at St Enoch, Glasgow. *R S Stephen Collection, NRM, RDS/C22*

CLIMAX AND CRISIS
1901–1942

The frenetic events of 1899 - 1900 had two far reaching implications for the British locomotive industry, - the amalgamation of the three Glasgow builders, and the formulation of a range of standard locomotives for the Indian railways. These two events were certainly related, but barely a decade later there was already some uncertainty as to who should be credited with initiating the concept of the Indian standards.

The motive power crisis on the home railways was already subsiding by mid-1901 when recrimination arose regarding the supply of locomotives to that most sacrosanct of markets, India. The Indian Government, or more specifically, the Secretary of State for India, Lord George Hamilton was taken to task for awarding both locomotive and bridge building contracts to foreign, ie American and German, industry. The British locomotive builders bitterly complained that different Indian railways laid down highly specific requirements which made their task well nigh impossible, whereas considerable latitude was permitted the American builders to conform to their own traditional standards.

Glasgow & South Western Railway 4-6-0 No 384, completed by the newly formed North British Locomotive Co in 1903, stands in Carlisle Citadel station in 1906.   *NRM/LGRP 28008*

The Indian Standard locomotives evolved in the early 1900s closely followed domestic British practice of the period, the 'Mail' 4-6-0 in particular.

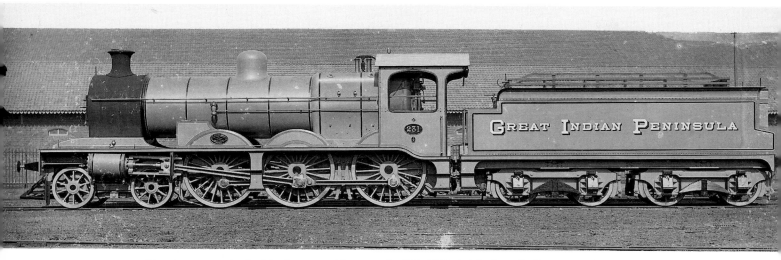

Showing an unmistakeable close resemblance to the G & SWR 4-6-0, Great Indian Peninsula Railway 4-6-0 No 231, also originally designed by Sharp Stewart & Co, but built by the North British Locomotive Co in 1905, pictured in photographic grey in India.

Both the G & SW and GIP 4-6-0s were designed in the same drawing office in Glasgow, but again showing a certain affinity is Manchester designed and built 4-6-0 No 1103 of the Great Central Railway (Beyer, Peacock & Co, 1906). *NRM 84/3047*

The Engineer (7 June 1901) reiterated its 1899 criticism of London-based consulting civil engineers who justified their own existence by prescribing unnecessarily elaborate standards. Having said this, however, the Pittsburgh Locomotive Works was able to supply the (Indian) North Western Railway with a batch of eight very attractive 2-8-2Ts which incorporated high quality British-made materials. The rather high-handed view of certain of the British builders, particularly those in Glasgow, was that traditional customers should be prepared to wait if they wanted quality, regardless of rapidly increasing traffic levels as were occurring in India at that time.

It was at this point, around mid-1901, that the three Glasgow locomotive builders, Dübs & Co, Neilson, Reid & Co, and Sharp, Stewart & Co, seriously discussed (not for the first time) merging with each other, and mooted the idea of standardising locomotives for India, both on the broad (5ft 6in) and metre rail gauges. This matter was duly discussed at a conference held in Calcutta in December 1901. Stemming from this a series of 4-4-0, 4-4-2, 0-6-0, 4-6-0 and 2-8-0 designs was evolved over

the next few years which would not have looked out of place on certain British lines, particularly the Great Central Railway.

Precisely what the links were is now difficult to establish, but they undoubtedly existed. For instance there were very close similarities between 4-6-0s ordered almost simultaneously in late 1902 from Sharp, Stewart & Co by the Bengal Nagpur Railway and the Glasgow & South Western Railway. Even the contemporary technical press became confused, for example, the chimneys appear to have been cast to the same pattern and the general styling was remarkably similar.

The BNR was particularly progressive. Its 4-6-0 actually predated the Indian standards, but it set the basic pattern for many hundreds of 'Mail' 4-6-0s, which would be built in Britain for India until 1950. Also in 1902 the BNR had placed orders with Robert Stephenson & Co for a heavy goods 2-8-0 which was likewise a trend-setter, but to a rather lesser degree.

For their part, the G & SWR 4-6-0s ranked amongst the very first locomotives to carry North British Locomotive Company builder's plates following the formation of the new combine on 1 April 1903. The name of the new enterprise had only been selected with some difficulty, although it should be recalled that prior to 1914 Scotland was often referred to as 'North Britain'.

The formation of the North British Locomotive Company in 1903 roughly coincided with the actual highpoint of the British locomotive industry, or perhaps more accurately, the beginning of its long decline. This, however, was far from immediately evident at that time. The new enterprise, with three works in Glasgow, had the theoretical capacity to build 700 new locomotives per annum, or about half the total national capability. This would never be realised, NBL's actual maximum annual production would be but 573 units in 1905.

Commercial locomotive production in Britain peaked in 1907, in terms of the number of locomotives built (1,300), when coincidentally the American locomotive industry also reproduced an all time record total of 7,360 locomotives, mainly for domestic service.

Ironically, in view of the events of 1899 - 1900, the American, or more specifically Baldwin threat, was not sustained. More significant in accounting for a fall-off in orders on British builders was the increasing self-sufficiency of formerly heavily reliant countries. The two most diverse examples were perhaps Japan and Holland, which had begun indigenous production around 1892 and 1900 respectively. Holland also showed an increasing tendency after 1900 to favour German manufacturers on account of the lower prices which they quoted due to lower labour costs.

By 1909, trade in general was in the grip of a recession, which worsened in 1910 before showing slight signs of improving again. The year 1911 witnessed industrial unrest, on the railways in particular during an exceptionally hot August, whilst 1912 saw strife in the coal industry. In early 1913 the NBL celebrated the completion of its works number 20,000, a 4-8-2 for the Rhodesia Railways. Reporting this event *The Railway Gazette* for 7 March 1913, remarked:

'Today with 20,000 to their credit, we may venture to express the hope that another decade may, with favourable markets, enable this world-renowned establishment to report a further advance to 30,000'. (Just *fifty* years later, NBL had recently passed out of existence, and had still not reached the 30,000 mark).

The watershed year of 1913 reflected a distinct upturn in locomotive demand, particularly from India, which ironically resulted in just a hint of 1899 all over again. Once more British manufacturers could not promise quick delivery, although demand was not as high as previously, with the result that two British railways turned to Germany! In time for the 1914 summer traffic, the South Eastern & Chatham Railway sought 22 large superheater 4-4-0s. Orders for twelve went to Beyer, Peacock & Co of Manchester in October 1913 and for ten more to Borsig of Berlin, in February 1914. The latter were delivered first, being erected under German supervision at Ashford Works. They had scarcely completed their trials when Britain declared war on Germany. (They were not paid for until after the 1918 Armistice with interest accrued). Never one to mince its words *The Railway Engineer* for June 1914, regardless of growing public animosity towards Germany, fearlessly observed:

'Sentiment may keep orders in this country, but the SE & CR cannot afford much for such luxuries. Moreover the time when British builders could reasonably claim anything extra for superior material or workmanship has passed, for Berlin and Munich turn out locomotives equal in every respect to those from Glasgow or Manchester'.

In addition to the SE & CR the Taff Vale Railway placed an order in Germany in 1914, with the Hohenzollern Locomotive Works for six 0-6-2Ts. This was later rescinded and transferred to NBL.

The outbreak of hostilities in August 1914 resulted in a reduction once again in locomotive output, not that the private manufacturers became underemployed, their specialist facilities, as were those of certain railway works, were now devoted to munitions production and other government work. Thus locomotive production at Kitsons' declined from 97 in 1915 (which it would never again approach) to nil in 1916, when both it and Beyer, Peacock became heavily committed to war work. At this time the LNWR placed an order on BP for twenty 0-8-0s, but no significant progress was ever made on these and the order eventually reverted to Crewe Works. Conversely the industrial locomotive builders 'never had it so good', collectively averaging 300 locomotives per year during 1916-18 due to government contracts, eg 100 75cm gauge 4-6-0Ts by the Hunslet Engine Company for the War Department.

A considerable proportion of the output of the larger builders during 1917-19 was 2-8-0s of Great Central Railway design for the Railway Operating Division of the British Army for service in France. In more recent times often referred to as the RODs, at the time the term 'MM' was more commonly applied, being the abbreviation for Ministry of Munitions. Their construction was divided as follows:-

Kitson & Co	32 engines	1918
Robert Stephenson & Co	82	1917 - 20
Nasmyth Wilson & Co	32	1917 - 18
North British Loco Co	369	1917 - 19
	515	

The French railways also placed extensive orders with British builders for 2-8-0s, 4-6-0s, and 4-6-2s. Some of the 2-8-0s built by NBL, Vulcan Foundry and Nasmyth Wilson would remain in service in France until the early 1970s.

During World War 1 Britain's railways came under direct government control via the Railway Executive Committee. This had initially seriously restricted locomotive construction with regard to reduced manpower and material levels and the priorities accorded munition manufacture. In late June 1917, however, it indicated a willingness to permit a measure of relaxation in this regard. It was at this time that there were calls to establish a range of national standard locomotives to facilitate post-war construction, which would also conform to a national loading gauge. One consideration here was the possibility of the long discussed Channel Tunnel being revived to unite post-war Europe.

During the winter of 1917-18 several railway drawing offices evolved 4-4-0, 2-6-0, 4-6-0, and 2-8-0 schemes under the auspices of the Association of Railway Locomotive Engineers (ARLE). The private locomotive industry made no input into these, of which a mixed traffic 2-6-0 and heavy goods 2-8-0 were deemed to be the priorities. After the Armistice, in order to maintain employment at Woolwich Arsenal the government announced in late 1919 that it intended to commence railway locomotive and rolling stock construction and repair there.

As a starting point, for simplicity it was decided to build 100 2-6-0s of SE & CR design. Although capable of manufacturing heavy calibre naval guns, the construction of locomotive boilers fell outside Woolwich's competence. These were therefore ordered from North British (85) and Robert Stephenson & Co

(15). In the event, despite its good intentions, the Woolwich project proved to be an expensive fiasco, although most of the engines ultimately found buyers in England and Ireland.

More serious as far as the traditional builders were concerned was the incursion into their domain after 1918 of two privately owned shipbuilders and munitions manufacturers, Armstrong Whitworth & Co of Scotswood, Newcastle-upon-Tyne, and William Beardmore & Co of Dalmuir, Glasgow to whom steam locomotives were small beer after battleships. (A third, Vickers at Barrow, had also contemplated locomotive building). Armstrong's board only resolved in October 1918 to engage in locomotive manufacture, yet its first engine, an 0-8-0 for the neighbouring North Eastern Railway, was ceremoniously steamed off the plant only just over a year later on 4 November 1919. Such was their rapid penetration of the locomotive market that in 1920 Armstrong's and Beardmore's collectively accounted for nearly 25 per cent of the total production of the large locomotive builders, and almost 50 per cent of their (reduced) 1922 output. Their secret was modern plant and equipment as a result of the recent war, which enabled them to secure some of the largest locomotive contracts in recent years, which were funded in many cases by post-war government compensation payments. On the 'home front' Beardmore's received an order from the LNWR for 90 'Prince of Wales' 4-6-0s and 60 tenders, then valued at £900,000. Armstrong's had similarly received an order for 50 0-8-0s from the North Eastern Railway. Both of these contracts, however, paled in comparison with the 200 2-8-0s ordered by the Belgian State Railways in February 1920, which Armstrong's 'snatched' from continental builders according to contemporary reports. With their shipbuilding background both enterprises could directly load (dismantled) locomotives on ships (sometimes of their own manufacture also!) moored alongside their works.

Whereas Beardmore's built locomotives only to drawings supplied, Armstrong's set up a new locomotive design department, 'poaching' drawing office staff from long-established builders in the North East. The general manager of the locomotive department of Armstrong, Whitworth & Co was Robert B McColl, a Scot and former G & SWR apprentice who had spent some time in the drawing office at Stephenson's c. 1904. Recruited specially by Armstrong's he later moved to the American Locomotive Company at Schenectady, of which he became President in late 1945. In addition to showing locally an unmistakably aggressive stance, looking ahead to eventual electric and even diesel locomotive construction, Armstrong's added insult to injury by announcing that they proposed to establish a locomotive building plant in India, which in the event came to nothing.

In early 1920 Armstrong's entered into negotiations with the new Soviet Government in Russia regarding the supply of new 0-10-0s, at a rate which the Russians hoped would reach 60 per month. However, owing to the interference by the British Government, Armstrong's merely built 50 boilers which were incorporated on 500 0-10-0s being built in Sweden.

The immediate post-war boom in locomotive building, as in other industries, particularly ship building, was over all too soon and by 1922 there was a deep economic recession. Two years earlier China had been identified as a major potential market for the future. In its editorial *The Engineer* for 20 August 1920 had sagely predicted:-

"In a few years British manufacturers will be scouring the world for orders. They must keep an eye on the leaner years ahead of them. The future never looks after itself. It cannot be left to chance. It is only by making provision now.........that one can avoid disappointment. It is necessary to say this, for we have received within the last few days convincing proofs that British engineers are not making all the exertions in China that are needed".

At a recent conference to consider standardisation of certain parts of locomotives at which representatives of British and American firms had been present:

"the Americans showed by their zeal and thoroughness that they were very dangerous competitors. They left no stone unturned to make themselves conversant with the influence of the conference nor to get into touch with the engineers and commercial people connected with the railways.....Very many of the engineers of Chinese railways prefer to buy British material. But Chinese directors have not the same ties; they are quite prepared to purchase in the market that which suits them best. Manufacturers must act for themselves and act energetically.

There is no engine made by British engineers which is constructed with greater care than the locomotive. Our makers rejoice in having every part of the very best, in imparting a high degree of finish, and assuring themselves by steaming tests that all the engines are in proper adjustment. The Americans, as is well known, are not nearly so particular. They consider our degree of finish an expensive luxury, (and) are content to use material that we object to using. They do not take the same care with their adjustments, and in many cases, we believe, give, if they give at all, a very perfunctory steaming trial. It is common knowledge that, by contrast with British locomotives, American engines are crude and unfinished. We should be very sorry indeed to see any lowering of the British standard of excellence,......but how we are to maintain the same standards of workmanship and the same excellence of material and yet compete with the Americans is a problem for the manufacturer. It could be done fairly well in the old days, when the output per man was greater than it is now and the wages far less......We may yet be constrained to follow the American example and turn out engines finished in no respect as carefully as of yore."

It is interesting to note that the only *significant* locomotives order subsequently received from China, (without any fear of foreign competition) was for locomotives designed in China by British engineers fully conversant with local conditions, and the engines themselves were American in concept if not in manufacture (see Chapter 8).

The undeniable complacency of British manufacturers and *The Engineer* seriously questioning the absolute justification for the 'perfection' of their products was strongly reminiscent of 1901. But the British philosophy got quite a boost about 18 months later when it was revealed that there was a very strong prejudice in favour of British-built locomotives in South Africa. This followed the necessary importation of 98 locomotives from the US during 1918 - 1920, of which 58 were immediately found on arrival to be defective, requiring the re-staying of their fireboxes. The other 40 were later discovered to be defective also, resulting in major claims on the manufacturers.

Nevertheless this did not prevent the South African Railways soon afterwards from placing orders for 4-8-2s, not only in the United States, but with builders in such countries as Italy and Switzerland! Indeed these same builders bid for contracts to

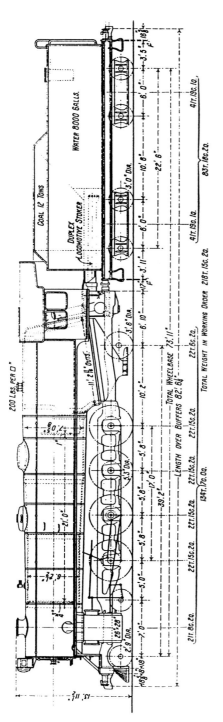

Between the two world wars the British locomotive industry showed its ability to incorporate American design philosophy in its products, particularly bar frames and mechanical stokers, in locomotives which were considerably larger than anything built for domestic service in Britain.

South Australian Railways 5ft 3in gauge 4-8-2 built Armstrong Whitworth & Co in 1926. In certain dimensional respects these ten engines exceeded the 4-8-4s built for China by the Vulcan Foundry ten years later. These 4-8-2s were themselves soon altered to 4-8-4 after their entry into service. Their cast bar frames were manufactured in the USA. The builders were awarded the contract against strong overseas competitors.

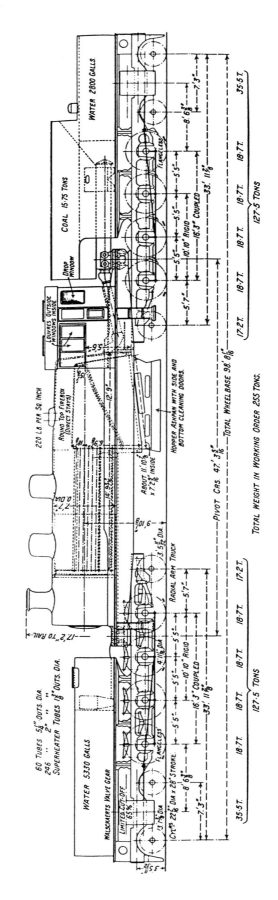

The experimental 5ft gauge 4-8-2 + 2-8-4 built for service in Siberia in 1932, which was the largest Beyer Garratt ever built. It too incorporated bar frames and was believed to be the first British locomotive to have cast steel cylinders. No repeat orders followed, but it saved its builders from extinction.

build 37 broad gauge inside-cylinder 0-6-0s for India, as was revealed in an illuminating table published in *The Railway Gazette* for 9 March 1923, of which details are given below.

TABLE 7 — Quotations for 37 5ft 6in gauge Inside-Cylinder 0-6-0 Tender Locomotives for the Oudh & Rohilkund and North Western Railway of India (1922)

Builder	Price each £	Port of Despatch	Delivery (weeks)
Vulcan Foundry	4,041	Mersey	20-29
Armstrong,Whitworth & Co	4,190	Newcastle	20-28
North British Loco Co	4,410	Glasgow	24-36
Group Français	4,566	Antwerp	36-64
Schneider & Co	4,606	Antwerp	54-96
Berliner Maschinenfabrik	4,670	Hamburg	30-48
Skoda & Co	4,729	Hamburg	32-46
Kitson & Co	4,758	Hull	22-46
W Beardmore & Co	4,810	Glasgow	30-48
Les Ateliers (Belgium)	4,900	Antwerp	36-84
La Meuse	5,015	Antwerp	32-104
Borsig & Co	5,025	Hamburg	36-54
Krupp & Co	5,030	Hamburg	36-54
Arn Jung	5,050	Hamburg	36-54
Rheinische	5,075	Hamburg	36-54
Hohenzollern	5,125	Hamburg	36-54
Ernesto Breda & Co	5,230	Genoa	44-72
Sachsische	5,290	Hamburg	36-50
Nasmyth Wilson & Co(10 only)	5,290	Mersey	17-30
Ansaldo	5,336	Genoa	65-95
Swiss Locomotive Company	5,491	Antwerp	28-64
Beyer, Peacock & Co	5,755	Manchester	35-67
Robt. Stephenson & Co	5,786	Middlesbrough	32-54
Hawthorn Leslie & Co	5,852	Middlesbrough	26-52
Nydquist & Holm	5,855	Gothenburg	32-84
Baldwin Locomotive Works	7,143	New York	16-28
Metallurgique du Hainaut	7,520	Antwerp	26-72

In this instance, Armstrong's, with the second lowest tender, secured the order. Soon afterwards this firm changed its policy to only taking orders at cost plus 10 per cent, which made it less competitive in a world of cut throat competition. Nevertheless, in 1923 it had secured a plum contract from the South Australian Railways to supply thirty heavy American-style 5ft 3in gauge 4-6-2s, 2-8-2s and 4-8-2s (ten of each).

By 1925 the excess manufacturing capacity of the *world* locomotive industry was openly acknowledged, and on this account South Africa decided against establishing its own locomotive building facility in the knowledge that locomotives could be imported at highly competitive prices. Interestingly, the world's total steam locomotive stock had probably reached its numerical peak (c. 250,000) in 1924, as it certainly did then in both North America and in Great Britain. It thereafter began to decline significantly due to a variety of factors, both economic, the rise of alternative forms of motive power, and the advent of road transport competition.

In 1922 it had been revealed that an order for 400 locomotives, then valued at £5 million, was likely to be placed by Romania with five British builders, with the possibility of more partially constructed at Woolwich Arsenal. (This may have given rise to the persistent story that parts for several Maunsell 2-6-0s were indeed sold to Romania). The Romanians requested deferred credit, and the problems of finance led to orders going instead to Germany, which supplied Prussian-type 0-10-0s rather

than the Somerset & Dorset type 2-8-0s on offer from Britain (see Chapter 7).

E L Ahrons, writing in *The Engineer* for 31 March 1922, pessimistically observed that 'the new Act for the grouping of the railways has every appearance of threatening to wipe out in the near future the remaining trade of the private locomotive builders with those railways which from time to time have placed their orders outside.' An ominous clause in the Act made provision for the pooling of workshop facilities.

Ahrons, who died in 1926, did not live to see that he would be proved wrong, if only via government intervention in order to maintain employment. This was achieved via the Development (Loans Guarantees and Grants) Act 1929, and the Railway Agreement Act 1935, which made interest-free loans available from the government to be spent on major capital projects, eg electrification, and the purchase or manufacture of new locomotives and rolling stock. Taking the period 1923-38, for example, no less than *one third* of the North British Locomotive Company's (reduced) production was for the home railways, including twenty 4-6-2s and ten 4-6-0s for the LNER, thirty 4-6-0s for the Southern and fifty 4-6-0s for the LMS to secure rapid delivery, before 1929 and prior to government intervention. Remarkably NBL took no advantage of the LMS 'Royal Scot' contract, which only it could have handled. It charged its desperate customer only £386,250 as against an actual cost of £385,237, thus making a profit of only £1,013, or merely $\frac{1}{4}$ per cent!

In 1929 the Great Western Railway placed orders for no fewer than 250 0-6-0 PTs with *six* different builders, including one (W.G. Bagnall Ltd) of which the GWR's Chief Mechanical Engineer, C B Collett, had reputedly never previously heard.

TABLE 8 — Allocation of Steam Locomotive Orders by 'Big Four' Railway Companies to Contractors, 1923 - 1938

	LMS	LNER	GWR	SR	TOTAL
North British Loco Co.	353	50	100	45	548
Sir W G Armstrong Whitworth & Co	327	52	75	9*	463
Vulcan Foundry	311				311
W Beardmore & Co	91	20			111
Beyer, Peacock & Co	33	51	25		109
Hunslet Engine Co	80				80
W G Bagnall Ltd	34		50		84
Kerr Stuart & Co	50		25		75
R Stephenson & Co	5	51			56
Yorkshire Engine Co		9	25		34
R & W Hawthorn Leslie & Co		33			33
A Barclay & Sons	25				25
Kitson & Co	5	12			17
Nasmyth Wilson & Co	15				15
Avonside Engine Co		6			6
Manning Wardle Ltd				1	1
TOTAL	1329	278	306	55	1968

* These locomotives were merely erected from parts supplied
Note: LMS totals include engines ordered for Somerset & Dorset Joint Railway

It was in August 1929 that the Bank of England, under its Governor, Montagu Norman, made initial plans to attempt to rationalise the British locomotive industry. His provisional scheme was to merge the five or six leading builders (but excluding Armstrong, Whitworth & Co in view of its other diverse interests) to

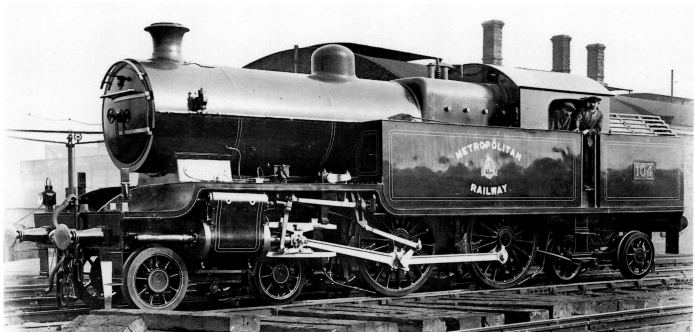

A brand new 4-4-4T for the Metropolitan Railway, one of eight delivered by Kerr Stuart & Co of Stoke on Trent in 1920-21. Construction was dogged by materials shortages and rapidly increasing prices. The original livery of these engines was a rich Indian red.

NRM/LPC 70022

A Hull & Barnsley Railway inside-cylinder 0-8-0, one of fifteen delivered by the Yorkshire Engine Company of Sheffield in 1907 to cope with an export coal boom. These were the largest locomotives to be designed by a member of the Stirling family (Matthew), hence the domeless boiler, and the only ones to incorporate the Belpaire firebox.   *NRM/LPC 62206*

EXAMPLES OF LARGE LOCOMOTIVES FOR SMALLER BRITISH RAILWAY COMPANIES BY SOME OF THE SMALLER LOCOMOTIVE BUILDERS.

Arguably one of the most handsome British 4-6-0 designs ever built was the Highland Railway 'Clan' which was entirely designed as well as built by R & W Hawthorn Leslie & Co in Newcastle. No 55 *Clan Mackinnon* poses new at Perth in 1921.   *NRM/LPC 0714*

form a holding company. The latter would acquire the shares of each of the constituent companies, which would nevertheless continue to exist as separate trading entities. In view of the dominant position of the North British Locomotive Company its Chairman Sir Hugh Reid was approached to become Chairman of the new enterprise. On personally putting the invitation to Sir Hugh in Glasgow, Norman received short shrift having it pointed out to him that NBL had already rationalised, - back in 1903. Even North British paid no dividend to its ordinary shareholders throughout the 1930s.

By 1932-33 there were years when neither North British, Armstrong's, nor Robert Stephenson & Co each built a single steam locomotive. In 1933 for the first time not one steam locomotive was supplied by the private builders to the home railways. In 1932, Kitson & Co, which had received no *major* orders since about 1924, built five 0-4-0STs for the LMS, having acquired the goodwill of Manning Wardle Ltd back in 1926. Beyer, Peacock & Co came perilously close to closing down altogether but was kept going by an order from Soviet Russia for an exceptionally large 4-8-2 + 2-8-4 Beyer Garratt, and a number of heavy industrial 0-4-0Ts and 0-6-0Ts to offset its high development costs. The writer has it on good authority that an unidentified individual was on the point of unilaterally closing down the firm when he received a telegram, which had actually been accepted by the Post Office, from the Chairman, Sir Sam Fay, which explicitly threatened him with extreme personal violence if he did so! The would be victim desisted, the firm was saved, and Fay resigned soon afterwards on account of his private life.

Kerr Stuart & Co had already 'gone under' in 1931, allegedly as the result of internal maladministration, and the Avonside Engine Company folded in 1935.

In late 1934 Armstrong Whitworth & Co secured an order from the LMS for 100 Class 5 4-6-0s, allegedly as a result of a quotation made over the telephone which had omitted to take into account the cost of the tenders. Even before this order was completed, Armstrong's landed yet another, for no fewer than 227 4-6-0s, the manufacture of all castings for which was subcontracted to a foundry in Letchworth. On delivery of the final 4-6-0, in December 1937, Armstrong's withdrew from active locomotive manufacture, but at a price, as will be related in Chapter 6. It was quickly followed in 1938 by Kitson's in Leeds and Nasmyth Wilson & Co in Manchester. Another indication of the long overdue rationalisation of the locomotive industry finally achieved by Montagu Norman was the amalgamation of Robert Stephenson & Co and Hawthorn Leslie & Co in 1937 to form Robert Stephenson & Hawthorns Ltd.

During the 1930s (ie the decade 1931-40) British railway works built considerably more new locomotives (2,900) than did the private major locomotive builders (2,000). The latter's all-time low point was hit in 1932 with a collective output of only 39 locomotives (compared with 1,032 only 25 years previously) and compared with 268 by the railways themselves. The American and German industries had all but entered hibernation in 1933, but at least did not have to face the same galling scenario as their British counterpart.

In late 1936 the Institution of Locomotive Engineers held a 'confidential conference' concerning the vexed question of the home railways building their own locomotives at a time when the private builders still had their backs to the wall. The ethics of this also received an airing in the railway and national press with leading articles entitled 'Who Shall Build?' etc. Although once more it had no orders whatever from the home railways, by 1938 as far as export orders were concerned matters appeared to be improving somewhat for the British locomotive industry. North British received orders from New Zealand for 40 semi-streamlined 4-8-2s and from South Africa for 44 Class 15F heavy 4-8-2s. On the other hand the SAR had ordered no fewer than 137 heavy (Class 15F and 23) 4-8-2s from German builders, one consequence of which was that the total value of German locomotive exports in 1938 exceeded British for the first time and so led the world. (American locomotive export activity throughout the 1930s was at a very low level).

A change of CME in South Africa also resulted in renewed orders on Beyer, Peacock for Garratts, which was quickly followed by orders for such from Rhodesia and East Africa. In 1940 Turkey made enquiries for 2-10-0s from three British builders, which included BP, which also received an order from Iran (then still known as Persia) for 24 2-10-2s. By this time Britain was once again at war with Germany and work on these contracts had to be suspended until after the cessation of hostilities.

Yet it was not an ill wind, for with the onset of war the newly formed Ministry of Supply quickly placed orders with NBL for 150, and with Beyer, Peacock & Co, for 50 2-8-0s of LMS Class 8F 2-8-0 design for service overseas. However it was not until mid-1942 that the British locomotive industry *as a whole* began to return to something like normality, if indeed 'normality' could ever be defined in the context of locomotive manufacture.

THE FINAL FLOURISH
1943–1958

The British private steam locomotive building industry experienced a final flowering during the decade immediately after the end of World War 2, before rapidly withering and ultimately vanishing almost without trace. This was largely due to the increasingly rapid transition from steam to diesel power almost worldwide after 1945. This process had begun in the United States, where the commercial construction of steam locomotives even for export, had attained negligible proportions even by 1952. As of January 1949 eleven different builders had on hand orders for some 1500 steam locomotives valued at £26 million at contemporary prices. More significant orders were yet to follow up to about 1955, especially for Beyer Garratts, and particularly from Australia. However by January 1959 only one small builder had two narrow gauge 2-8-4Ts on hand valued at £34,000!

The formal and highly detailed contemporary technical descriptions of these final orders, replete with broadside official photographs, weight diagrams and occasionally sectional general arrangement drawings, published in *The Locomotive Magazine* and *The Railway Gazette*, gave no hint of the acute problems which confronted an industry which was then unknowingly entering its death throes.

The beginnings of the final resurgence can be traced back to the midpoint of the war, mid-1942, which was also a military turning point for the Allies. This in itself posed the question of, as in World War 1, providing (2-8-0) locomotives for military service in Continental Europe. An austerity version of the LMS Class 8F Belpaire taper boiler 2-8-0 was schemed by F G Carrier in the LMS Design Office at Derby in late July 1942. With a 15.6 ton axleload this incorporated a simple parallel round-topped boiler, fabricated components in place of castings, and cast iron in place of cast steel wherever possible. Although the total cost was remarkably little different from that of an LMS '8F' the number of man hours required to build an 'Austerity' was significantly reduced. The Ministry of Supply placed a pilot order for 300 locomotives with NBL, which duly handed over the first one only five months later on 16 January 1943. Further orders quickly followed to both NBL and the Vulcan Foundry, which collectively produced no fewer than 465 of these engines

during 1943 alone. Altogether 935 engines (545 NBL/390 VF) to a total value of £8.75 million including spares, were produced in three years (1943 - 45) together with 150 13½ ton axleload 2-10-0 derivatives from NBL alone. Of these 733 2-8-0s and 25 2-10-0s eventually passed into British Railways service as second hand purchases. In addition the MoS ordered 377 0-6-0STs of Hunslet design from six builders including the Vulcan Foundry, which in 1944 had taken over Robert Stephenson & Hawthorns, another participant.

TABLE 9 — War Department Austerity Locomotives Built 1943-46

Type	Builder	Quantity	Total	Built
2-10-0	N B Loco Co	150	150	1943-45
2-8-0	N B Loco Co	545		1943-45
	Vulcan Foundry	390	935	1943-45
0-6-0ST	Vulcan Foundry	50		1945
	Hunslet Engine Co	120		1943-45
	Andrew Barclay	15		1945-46
	Robert Stephenson & Hawthorns	90		1943-45
	Hudswell Clarke & Co	50		1943-46
	W G Bagnall Ltd	52	377	1944-46
			1462	

For its part Beyer, Peacock & Co, quite apart from producing large quantities of munitions, also built a number of Garratts to MoS order which succeeded in reaching for the most part their designated railways in the Far East. Indeed surprisingly few locomotives were lost at sea through enemy action during the war. Ironically, one RSH-built light 4-8-2 for the South African Railways (No 2734) was lost in transit in the early days of peace in February 1946 and a replacement for it was built to special order later the same year.

No doubt with memories of the dire boom and bust situation which had developed under similar circumstances 25 years earlier, in March 1945 the locomotive manufacturers made approaches to the British main line railways with a view to

A brand new Glasgow built 5ft 6in gauge Class WG 2-8-2 for India on display at South Bank, London, during the Festival of Britain in 1951. This was the last major occasion on which a British-built steam locomotive for the export market would be exhibited any-where, a tradition which dated back a century to the Great Exhibi-tion of 1851 in Hyde Park. Within a year or so there was a recognition that the steam locomotive almost everywhere was living on borrowed time, the picture would be very different less then ten years later. *P Ransome Wallis Collection, NRM (PRW 3626)*

obtaining some firm locomotive orders from them. During the war, then coming to an end, new locomotive construction had fallen badly into arrears, with the average age of the LNER loco-motive stock, for example increasing from 27.7 years at end 1939 to 32.4 years at end 1945. Huge numbers of locomotives were also overdue for heavy repairs and so the railway works sim-ply could not be expected to have sufficient capacity for some time to come. The LNER had recently decided to procure one thousand new locomotives over the next five years in order to permit the scrapping of a similar number of obsolete types. Under Edward Thompson, CME in succession to Sir Nigel Gresley following the latter's death in 1941, a similar standardi-

sation policy was being pursued as that inaugurated a decade be-fore on the LMS under William Stanier, whom Thompson greatly admired. Having taken initial soundings regarding 300 4-6-0s in late 1944 the following orders were placed outside by the LNER:-

TABLE 10 — Post War LNER Locomotive Orders

	Qty	Builder	Date of Order	Delivered
Class K1 2-6-0	(70)	N B Loco Co	July 1947	1949-50
Class B1 4-6-0	(100)	N B Loco Co	Aug 1945	1946-47
Class B1 4-6-0	(150)	N B Loco Co	Jan 1946	1947-48
Class B1 4-6-0	(50)	Vulcan Foundry	Jan 1946	1947
Class B1 4-6-0	(40)	N B Loco Co	Sept 1948	1950-52
Class L1 2-6-4T	(35)	N B Loco Co	July 1947	1948-49
Class L1 2-6-4T	(35)	R Stephenson & Hawthorns	July 1947	1949-50

In the case of the 4-6-0s built by Vulcan Foundry, at least some had boilers supplied by the by the railway. Negotiations also took place with Beyer, Peacock & Co regarding the construction of twenty Class A2 mixed traffic 4-6-2s, but the builder was too

A 5ft 6in gauge three-cylinder 4-6-2 with Caprotti valve gear for the Argentine State Railways awaits shipment from the Gladstone Dock, Liverpool in September 1950. The high point of South American steam locomotive design, these Vulcan Foundry-built oil burners in the event saw little use owing to unfamiliarity with poppet valve gear and advancing dieselisation, on account of which the originally envisaged seventy engines were cut to only forty.

T J Edgington

busy to take on the order. Even so the grand total of 500 locomotives with three builders was very substantial, including 40 4-6-0s ordered shortly after nationalisation, which were the only steam locomotives ever ordered 'outside' by the newly formed British Railways.

During literally the last days of its independent existence in late 1947, the Great Western Railway placed orders for 200 94XX 0-6-0PTs with taper boilers with five different builders. Except for Robert Stephenson & Hawthorns these included the smaller industrial builders, but excluded the one remaining builder in GWR territory, Peckett & Sons of Bristol, which was not even invited to tender.

In practice this rather curious order, said to have been intended to replace the (200) remaining South Welsh 0-6-2T engines, appears to have been rather an expensive embarrassment; both to British Railways and to most of the builders involved, for much sub-contracting subsequently took place. Although the final engine was not delivered until late 1956, some earlier engines were in store by 1955, and one engine built that year was

withdrawn from service only *four* years later! The original total estimated price of £1,774,810 was exceeded by 28 per cent at £2,276,830. The final ten engines cost £13,588 each in 1956 as against a 1947 contract price of £8,720, even though, as in most cases, the customer had supplied the boilers as 'free issue'.

TABLE 11 — Construction of GWR 94XX 0-6-0PTs 1949 - 56 (Ordered December 1947)

Original Contractor	Qty	Sub-contractor	Delivered
R Stephenson & Hawthorns*	(80)	-	1950-53
Hunslet Engine Co	(10)	Yorkshire Engine Co	1954-55
W G Bagnall Ltd	(50)	-	1949-54
Yorkshire Engine Co	(30)	-	1949-54
Hudswell Clarke & Co	(20)	R Stephenson & Hawthorns	1950-52
Hunslet Engine Co	(10)	Yorkshire Engine Co	1955-56
	(200)		1949-56

* Newcastle and Darlington Works

In 1946 certain builders had to address the question of orders originally placed in 1939-40, ie 2-10-0s for Turkey, 2-10-2s for Iran, and (possibly) 5ft 6in gauge three-cylinder Caprotti 4-6-2s for Argentina. In the case of North British and Beyer, Peacock it actually became necessary to reserve a 'building space', so full had their order books suddenly become. Even so the next few years were fraught with problems, not least materials shortages, escalating prices, and the behaviour of certain customers.

Out of nearly 2300 steam locomotives which saw service in Ireland, some 1300 were produced by British manufacturers. A fitting climax to these were the five Class VS three-cylinder 4-4-0s for the Great Northern of Ireland built by Beyer, Peacock & Co. in 1948. Painted 'Caledonian' blue these were also the last and most advanced 4-4-0s in the world.

A Turkish State Railways (TCDD) 2-10-0, No 56089, at Ankara in 1958. Thirty seven of these engines were built by Beyer, Peacock & Co and Vulcan Foundry in 1948 to an order placed almost ten years earlier. These were the only modern British-built steam locomotives to be built to German drawings.

P Ransome Wallis Collection, NRM (PRW 5934)

Thus in April 1947 the Indian Government placed orders with NBL for no fewer than 125 of the new Class WP 4-6-2s, of which the pilot batch of sixteen was currently being built in the USA by Baldwins. This order was subsequently rescinded and transferred to North America in pursuit of quicker delivery, although the pilot order for 100 of the 2-8-2 freight equivalent, the WG, was 'firmly' placed instead with NBL in October 1948. Second only to India as a market for British-built locomotives was South America, Argentina in particular (where many of the railways had been British owned) although this country proved to be particularly erratic in the late 1940s. In May 1946 Robert Stephenson & Hawthorns received an order for ten Caprotti 4-6-2s from the Central Argentine Railway, as developments of twenty engines delivered by Armstrong Whitworth & Co in

1930. Slow progress was made in the drawing office in Darlington and two years later in early 1948 the order was transferred to the Vulcan Foundry, which had just received orders for 40 more as a standard (5ft 6in gauge) express passenger engine for the newly nationalised Argentine railways. Twenty more were ordered almost simultaneously from NBL, but later cancelled. Around 1949 Vulcan Foundry had some £600,000 due in outstanding payments from Argentina, for which it was also currently building 30 mixed traffic 4-8-0s, of which a further batch was also cancelled.

Vulcan appear to have been particularly unlucky, for in mid-1952 it concluded a contract for 30 2-8-2s for the Nigerian Railways, which subsequently pressed for quicker delivery which resulted in fifteen engines being subcontracted to Henschel in Germany. Even this paled when compared to the Iranian 2-10-2 saga. Beyer Peacock's deferred 1940 order for 24 2-10-2s had been passed after the war to Vulcan, and subsequently increased to 64 engines. Delivery commenced in 1950, but in 1953 owing to the Abadan oil crisis diplomatic relations were broken off between Britain and Iran. This left 24 2-10-2s still on the builder's hands, which had to be stored in temporary sidings (and shunted periodically on account of their roller bearings). The engines were eventually shipped in 1954, and paid for, but the class appears to have enjoyed but a brief working life, for only three were still operational in early 1961!

In 1948 there was a real possibility of NBL receiving an order from the Soviet Union for 1,100 narrow gauge (0-8-0) forestry locomotives, valued at £7 million. To accommodate these, reactivation of the defunct Atlas Works was contemplated. As with Armstrong's over 25 years earlier, this potentially highly lucrative contract came to nothing, one suspects again through government interference.

Post-war production peaked in 1949, after which other problems presented themselves. The early 1950s were plagued by a widespread shortage of steel plate which had the dual implication of making firm undertakings on price and delivery dates virtually impossible. In August 1953 the South African Minister of Transport publicly criticised British locomotive manufacturers for their inability to deliver on time, citing the new SAR Class 25 4-8-4 of which 100 (plus 40 tenders) had been ordered in November 1951 with delivery to commence in November 1952, of which only three had so far arrived.

Problems on delivery were a factor in the Indian Government placing large steam locomotive orders with European builders and Japan rather than with British manufacturers. By 1954 the world steel situation was easing and Japan, which was no longer building steam locomotives for its own use, was becoming a serious competitor, although its industry was suspected of being subsidised. In Britain the Locomotive Manufacturers Association tabulated the corresponding unit prices of Class WG 2-8-2s quoted in different countries at that time.

Japan	£28,890
Germany	£30,900 - £32,440
Great Britain	£31,489 - £33,000
United States	£63,191

It will be noted the American cost was in a league of its own, but in this instance it was of no direct concern to the customer as the engines were being funded by an international aid agency. A contract for 50 2-8-2s was awarded to alleviate hardship in *Philadelphia*, for by the 1950s under ordinary circumstances Baldwin was no longer competitive in the steam market and was also losing heavily to its domestic competitors, General Motors and former steam adversary ALCO in the diesel market. This once formidable enterprise quit the locomotive business in 1956, its final steam locomotives having been these 50 WGs completed in 1955. It had been to counter the perceived threat posed by the Baldwin Locomotive Works that had caused the North British Locomotive Company to come into being in 1903.

In addition to building the first batch of WGs in 1950 the North British Locomotive Co also supplied three complete sets of parts to the new Chittaranjan locomotive plant in India for assembly that year, and continued to supply it with boilers for some time. NBL also secured a contract from the Spanish National Railways (RENFE) for 25 2-8-2s, which were developed from the Indian 'XD' class. Not readily detectable in any statistics were 100 complete sets of parts for further engines which were erected in Spain by local builders, some of which subsequently built more in their own right during the late 1950s.

At this time NBL was working around the clock, on 4-8-4s for South Africa, and on 4-6-4s for Australia. The latter were 70 5ft 3in gauge engines for the Victorian State Railways of which delivery was still taking place in 1953, when they had already begun to be superseded by diesels. The whole sad saga only

finally emerged in 1985 when it became apparent that acrimonious correspondence had passed between customer and builder concerning both sub-standard workmanship, and bad stowage for the long sea crossing from Port Glasgow to Melbourne. The condition of some engines on arrival was very poor, and some enjoyed very short active lives, admittedly partly on account of rapidly increasing dieselisation.

Beyer, Peacock & Co meanwhile was enjoying something of a bonanza, especially as regards Garratts, some of which it was obliged to sub-contract to Belgian and German opposite numbers. It supplied many 4-8-2 + 2-8-4s to Africa in particular between 1950 and 1958, which ranged from 2ft gauge 66 ton engines for Sierra Leone to 252 ton metre gauge giants for the East African Railways, the remarkable 59 Class. Most, however, were 3ft 6in gauge GMAM engines for South Africa and 20 class for the Rhodesia Railways. Although those two designs were dimensionally similar, the latter suffered from boiler problems and in other respects were not entirely satisfactory.

A scheme for a modern 5ft 6in gauge 4-8-2 + 2-8-4 for India was not taken up, allegedly on account of its high cost. BP's total production for India had been surprisingly small, only about one tenth of that of the Vulcan Foundry (which it unsuccessfully attempted to take over in 1954) and less than its own for Ireland for example.

Standard gauge (4ft 8½ in) Garratts were relatively uncommon, but in 1949 Beyer, Peacock & Co received a major order for 50 4-8-4 + 4-8-4s from the New South Wales Government Railway, which had been one of its largest single customers in the late 19th century. These were the first Garratts to incorporate American-made cast steel engine beds, but after delivery commenced in 1952 the NSWGR attempted to renege on the order by cutting it back. Ultimately only 42 engines entered service, for which there was no shortage of spare parts, for only three engines were cancelled completely. Dieselisation and trades union problems were at the root of this unhappy saga.

Ironically, in anticipation of its approaching centenary in 1954, BP commissioned a colour documentary film describing the design, construction and commissioning of these majestic engines, which must have constituted a unique piece of cinema for those fortunate enough to have witnessed it.

For its part the North British Locomotive Company celebrated its Golden Jubilee in 1953 by publishing a lavish brochure which extolled its achievements, past and present. This included an interesting quantification of the destination of the locomotive which it and its three constituents had built over a period of 120 years:

Britain	9,550
India and Far East	7,900
Africa	3,400
North & South America & Miscellaneous	3,300
Europe	2,500
Australia & New Zealand	1,100

This rather neatly gives a relative magnitude *overall* of the different markets served by the British locomotive industry.

In 1955 Vulcan Foundry supplied the last of almost 3,000 steam locomotives to India since 1852. It, along with its own subsidiary, Robert Stephenson & Hawthorns, at this time was taken over by the English Electric Company (which had outbid Beyer, Peacock & Co). Vulcan by this time had relatively little

Just a century after Robert Stephenson & Co had supplied the first locomotive to Australia, it also supplied one of the last. This was a one-off non-superheated 2-6-2T for Hebburn Collieries in New South Wales, ordered in March 1954 and shipped in May 1955. It was actually descended from the Mersey Railway 2-6-2T of 1887, illustrated in Chapter 10.   *Hebburn Collieries*

steam work and at least one small order was transferred by the new management to Darlington. That works was also currently engaged on its last *significant* steam order, for 24 3ft 6in gauge 2-8-2s from the Western Australia Government Railways, which had been transferred to it by Beyer, Peacock in 1951.

It was by this time ten years since the end of World War 2, and the world was changing fast, not least regarding railway motive power. In December 1950 the LMA had informally approached British Railways as regards obtaining some orders for the forthcoming Standard steam locomotives, but was informed that there was little prospect before 1955 at least. However BR's own building programmes rapidly fell badly behind owing to the steel shortage, and to circumvent the rationing of this commod-

ity quotations were obtained in late 1953 for 35 2-10-0s each from NBL and the Vulcan Foundry, and for 50 Class 5 4-6-0s from Robert Stephenson & Hawthorns. In the event these were not taken up, and within twelve months British Railways took the momentous decision to phase out steam traction, making this public in January 1955.

Already dwindling, almost overnight the bottom dropped out of the steam locomotive export market, which was by then largely confined to British Commonwealth countries, which kept an eye on developments in Britain. The only substantial steam orders yet to follow were for more Garratts from Rhodesia and South Africa, although in view of their urgency some of the latter were subcontracted to North British and Henschel. Only ten years after the American Locomotive Company had despatched its final steam locomotive in 1948, North British, Beyer Peacock, and Robert Stephenson & Hawthorns each completed what proved to be their final steam locomotives during 1958, as did Henschel in Germany, - the trend was unmistakable. Beyer, Peacock and North British each produced the odd spare boiler during 1960, for Rhodesian Garratts and Sudanese 4-8-2s respectively, but even the major steam locomotive *spares* market appeared to have virtually evaporated as the 1960s dawned.

The new decade witnessed the virtual extinction of the traditional British locomotive industry. Both BP and NBL had already begun to adapt to the new order by building main line diesels, but North British went into voluntary liquidation in 1962. On the first day of the following year the time-honoured names of Vulcan Foundry, and Robert Stephenson & Hawthorns passed into history, along with W G Bagnall Ltd by becoming totally subsumed into the English Electric Co. Beyer, Peacock & Co ceased operations in 1966 ironically just as there were two minor enquiries for new 2ft gauge 2-6-2 + 2-6-2 Garratts. These were from Nepal (1), and South Africa (8), the latter being handled by the Hunslet Engine Co and its South African subsidiary.

Interestingly the large press blocks for Garratt boilers were purchased with others by the Hunslet Engine Co in Leeds, which had anticipated a continued demand for replacement boilers for British-built locomotives overseas. In the early 1960s Hunslet accordingly upgraded its boiler shop, and indeed for a time continued to receive the occasional small order for a narrow gauge or industrial tank locomotive. However apart from a few boilers for 4-6-2s and 4-8-2s in the Sudan and for the eight Gar-

ratts otherwise to be built in South Africa, there was little actual demand in the event. The end of steam locomotive construction had seemingly come with the despatch from Jack Lane of two non-superheated inside-cylinder 0-6-0STs to the National Coal Board in South Yorkshire in March 1964, which incorporated recently patented Hunslet anti-smoke emission equipment. However six years later an order was received for a diminutive 750mm gauge of 1905 Kerr Stuart design for service in Indonesia. By then only a handful of even Hunslet staff had steam experience but the engine was steamed with some ceremony in the works yard on
26 November 1971 prior to despatch.

In 1977 the writer witnessed the huge castings rusting in the maker's works yard, which by that time were the only tangible reminder anywhere in Britain of a once great industry on its home ground. Hunslet, actually also a diesel pioneer, would last for almost another twenty years. Peckett's, the Yorkshire Engine Company, and Hudswell Clarke & Co had all effectively passed out of existence during the 1960s, and so as the 20th century drew to a close of the former British steam locomotive builders only Barclay's in Kilmarnock still remained.

The last British-built steam locomotives to be exported to continental Europe were four 0-8-0Ts to the British-owned Tharsis Sulphur & Copper Co in Spain delivered in 1955. Having the unusual gauge of 4ft the basic design dated back to 1914, but this final batch incorporated such refinements as roller bearing big ends.

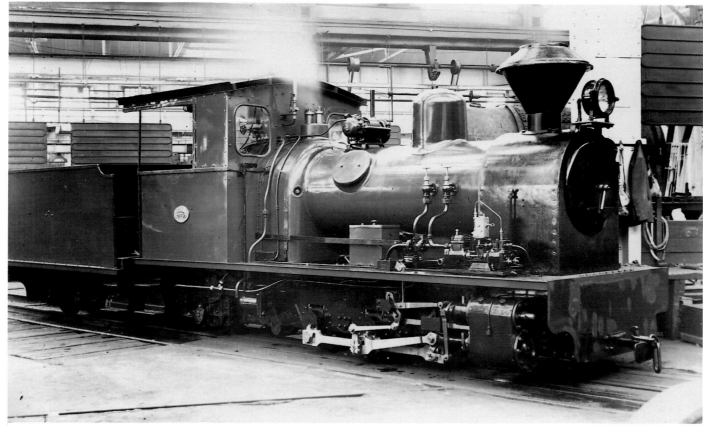

British Railways, Western Region, 0-6-0PT No 3409, delivered by the Yorkshire Engine Company of Sheffield in October 1956, almost *nine* years since it had originally been ordered by the Great Western Railway in December 1947. This was the last commercially built steam locomotive to be constructed for domestic main line service.

NRM SW E3/1272

OPPOSITE UPPER

The last *major* steam order to be undertaken by Robert Stephensons & Hawthorns at Darlington was for 24 3ft 6in gauge 2-8-2s for the Western Australian Government Railways. Originally ordered from and designed by Beyer, Peacock & Co these were sub-contracted by the latter in 1951 and delivered during 1955-56. They operated until 1971.

OPPOSITE LOWER

The last steam locomotive to be built in Scotland, a 600mm gauge 0-6-2 tender locomotive for a palm oil estate in Indonesia, completed by Andrew Barclay, Sons & Co in September 1962. A 1940 design by Bagnall's this repeat order was originally placed in Stafford but passed on to Kilmarnock by the English Electric Co, which had taken over Bagnall's. The boiler was designed to burn as fuel palm kernel shells, having a low calorific value which was a waste product of the industry.

TABLE 12 — British Commercial Steam Locomotive Manufacture 1948 - 1964

| Year | No | Locomotives | | Spare Boilers | |
		Total Wt (tons)	Value £	No	Value £
1948	484	38,223	7,529,690	N/A	N/A
1949	555	42,153	8,852,379	216	656,841
1950	524	41,333	9,566,172	215	693,305
1951	484	37,449	9,080,904	218	843,568
1952	389	29,403	7,579,626	217	887,776
1953	354	29,442	7,546,861	178	726,593
1954	377	33,314	9,541,456	215	990,924
1955	287	25,226	7,912,829	183	855,428
1956	101	11,150	3,750,103	150	715,821
1957	67	9,283	3,644,000	125	˙625,127
1958	43	4,592	1,912,000	74	495,084
1959	3	N/A	53,774	44	291,398
1960	2	N/A	17,728	16	81,303
1961	3	N/A	27,627	8	32,750
1962	5	158	72,083	14	55,062
1963	0	0	0	6	N/A
1964	2	76	28,870	4	N/A

1925

BRITISH RAILWAYS

NAMING CEREMONY

OF THE LAST STEAM

LOCOMOTIVE TO BE BUILT

BY BRITISH RAILWAYS

1960

SWINDON WORKS
(WESTERN REGION)
18TH MARCH 1960

Also sporting a GWR-style copper capped chimney was British Railways 2-10-0 No 92220 *Evening Star* completed at Swindon Works in March 1960, the last steam locomotive for BR. Ordinarily this would have been completed in 1958, like the 30 2-10-0s ordered *after* it, from Crewe Works. However, re-jigging of the Swindon plant for diesel locomotive production greatly delayed completion by at least 18 months.

TABLE 13 — Building Costs of Post World War 2 British-built Steam Locomotives for Overseas

Country/State	Gauge	Type	Empty Wt (tons)	Cost per engine (£)	Date
Turkey	4'8½"	2-10-0	123½	24,000	1948
Argentina	5'6"	4-8-0	110½	18,125	1949
Argentina	5'6"	4-6-2	134	35,600	1950
Victoria (Australia)	5'3"	4-6-4	135	28,950	1951
New South Wales (Australia)	4'8½"	4-8-4 +4-8-4	185	56,160	1952
Iran	4'8½"	2-10-2	133	33,384	1953
South Africa	3'6"	4-8-4 condensing	174¾	59,927	1954
East Africa	metre	4-8-2 +2-8-4	180	51,369	1955
South Africa	3'6"	4-8-2 +2-8-4	158½	59,610	1956
Rhodesia (Zimbabwe)	3'6"	4-8-2 +2-8-4	163¼	64,719	1957

Note: In actual terms the cost per ton (empty) of steam locomotives roughly doubled during the last decade of commercial steam locomotive construction, 1948-1957. During this same period the pound sterling had depreciated in value by some 33 per cent. The *real* increase in building cost was therefore of the order of 30 per cent.

THE LOCOMOTIVE MANUFACTURERS' ASSOCIATION

The self sufficiency of the larger home railways with regard to the manufacture of their own locomotives was a serious bone of contention with the private British builders for many years, but there was little they could do about it. However in the 1870s it was considered that the largest of all had overstepped the mark:

"Some time in the Month of April 1875 information was received that the London and North Western Railway Company had entered into competition with the Locomotive Manufacturers of the Country, and had undertaken to construct a number of Engines for the Lancashire and Yorkshire Railway Company; in consequence of this information Mr A Sacré of the Yorkshire Engine Company entered into communication with the various firms in England and Scotland with a view to gathering their opinion upon the legality of the action of the London and North Western Railway Company in respect of the Engines mentioned above which it was said they had undertaken to make."

Thus the Locomotive Manufacturers Association came into being, at the initial instigation of Alfred Sacré, Works Manager of the Yorkshire Engine Company. It held its inaugural meeting at Derby on 4 May 1875, and proceeded to take legal action against the LNWR succeeding in obtaining a High Court injunction preventing the latter from building locomotives for other than its own use. (In mitigation, it might be said, the building of engines for the LYR was mainly in anticipation of a merger of the two companies, which was for many years on the agenda and eventually occurred in 1922, one year before the general railway amalgamations of 1923).

Less well known is the fact that shortly after the LNWR case, similar action was taken against the Great Eastern Railway regarding its proposal to construct locomotives for the London, Tilbury & Southend Railway. The railway fought back and the case was not concluded until 1880, by which time the first 4-4-2Ts had already been ordered from Sharp Stewart & Co. Nothing quite so blatant ever happened again, but the LMA remained ever vigilant, in a few years casting its eyes rather further afield.

On occasions the LMA reacted to inaccurate information. In November 1907, for example, it debated the fact that during the previous year the Midland Railway had sold 50 (0-6-0 goods) engines to the Italian State Railway. These were stated to have been built in Glasgow as recently as 1900, but considerable re-

pairs had needed to be undertaken prior to their re-entry into service and the Midland could not be held to have purchased them originally with a view to sale. In fact the engines in question were Kirtley double-framed 0-6-0s averaging about 40 years old!

In March 1908 'it was reported to the Meeting that the Great Northern Railway were building at their Doncaster Works a number of locomotives (believed to be thirty) for the purpose of sale to the Great Central Railway.'

Attempts to obtain written clarification on the position via a solicitor failed, but verbal assurances were given by GNR and GCR that this was not the case. There was, however, no smoke without fire, for at this time the GNR and the GCR were actively considering amalgamation. Later in 1908 the Great Eastern Railway was also included in the scheme. However, when the bill was presented to Parliament in early 1909 it was vigorously opposed by the LMA and was indeed thrown out, although not necessarily for that reason.

Although 1907 witnessed an all time high in private British locomotive production, as that year drew to a close there was clearly a slump in orders. On 19 November 1907 the LMA minuted:

"Building by Home Railway Companies:-
In the course of general discussion it was shown that Members present were unanimously of opinion that it would be most opportune at the present time for the Association to make special efforts by the aid of the press and otherwise to bring to the notice of the general public and more particularly of the Share-holders and Directors of certain Home Railway Companies the excessive cost of the locomotives which those Companies build at their own works."

It was no coincidence that a short anonymous article entitled 'Should Railway Companies Build Their Own Locomotives?' appeared in *The Railway Gazette* for 3 January 1908. It suggested that given the existence of the well-established railway works, these should build only a modest number of locomotives to maintain a check on the prices charged by outside manufacturers.

Correspondence then ensued from various individuals identified only as 'Accountant (Retired)', 'Ex-Locomotive Superintendent', and 'Consulting Engineer' etc. Opinion was unanimously in favour of the private manufacturers.

A brand new German-built 4-4-0 for the South Eastern & Chatham Railway, No 778, after assembly by Borsig fitters, in the summer of 1914. *NRM 291/69*

The LMA Minutes are curiously silent as regards deliberations on American incursions into both the home and Indian markets around 1900. However, in July 1914, on the eve of war, German competition was hotly debated. 'German competition in the colonies and elsewhere was being strongly felt and likely to continue, most of all perhaps in India and South Africa.' In 1913 the total value of German locomotive exports had been very close behind those of Great Britain. The actual quantity, 1457, was far ahead of the 800 or so exported by the *major* British builders.

Mr Alec Campbell of the Hunslet Engine Company described a recent visit to Germany.

"The shops we visited were all excellent and extensions were general. We understood there were in all 21 shops building locomotives and that the Prussian State Railways required 1300 engines per annum. We considered the German Builders if not

actually combined were 'pulling together' and making an organised bid for British Markets. We regarded German work as only a colourable imitation of British but sufficiently near to be deceptive to ordinary Purchasers. German Makers get a 60 hour week out of their men and paid wages 15% less than obtained at home, and used a cheaper grade of materials throughout. They were looking with confidence for considerable increase in their export trade."

Only a month later Great Britain declared war on Germany and the problem, for the time being at least, became academic. Four years later in July 1918, in anticipation of the end of hostilities, locomotive standardisation was to the fore, both as regards domestic and overseas markets 'which would tend to decrease waste of time, labour, and material and would have a marked effect in increasing the general output of the Country.'

Peace became a reality four months later, and four days before the Armistice came into effect on 11 November, the LMA discussed the real possibility of some of the 'armament firms' taking up locomotive manufacture in the near future. In late January 1919 a meeting was hurriedly convened following information that representatives of member enterprises had entertained discussions with munitions manufacturers known to be interested in locomotive building regarding the loan of patterns etc.

In May 1919:

'It was decided to make strong recommendation to Members not to quote to the Loco-building Armament Firms for any locomotives or locomotive parts and to refrain, as far as might be possible, from purchasing materials from these Companies.'

Around this time the Vulcan Foundry was wrongly believed to have supplied boilers to William Beardmore & Co for the twenty 4-6-0s the latter was building for the Great Eastern Railway.

Worse was still to come, even before it had completed its first locomotive in Newcastle there were indications that Armstrong Whitworth & Co proposed to set up a locomotive-building plant in India with substantial assistance from the British Government. At the February 1920 meeting it was stated that this plan appeared to have been abandoned, but a new threat nearer home was debated, the government's proposal to convert Woolwich Arsenal to locomotive and rolling stock manufacture. Statistics were circulated to refute the Prime Minister's statement that the country's existing locomotive building capacity was so seriously overtaxed as to render State building at Woolwich necessary! By 1925 the LMA discussed the unquestioned *over* capacity of the locomotive building industry and possible rationalisation, but made no progress.

During 1920 - 21 there had been frequent references to the possibility of large contracts from Soviet Russia for new locomotives and locomotive repairs. This practically came to nothing on account of government interference.

In May 1921 the Railways Bill was described as 'a very serious menace to the Private Builders of the Country'. The amalgamation of the numerous railway companies into four large groups largely came into effect on 1 January 1923. The home railways and 'outside builders' continued to be regarded with great suspicion.

In December 1923 the highly salaried representatives of the locomotive builders, which included two knights of the realm, solemnly debated the fact that the GWR had recently supplied the Ottoman Railways with a cylinder block, presumed to have been from stock, for one of the Swindon-built Dean 0-6-0s which it had acquired from the British government during World War 1. Manufacturers had also been invited to quote, but as it was anticipated that the GWR was shortly to place extensive contracts outside (for boilers) it was decided not to pursue the matter further.

In January 1921 William Beardmore & Co had made an initial enquiry regarding membership of the LMA, and in the summer of 1923 the Chairman of the LMA met with the Chairmen of Messrs Armstrong's and Beardmore's 'but could see no signs of desire on their part to become Members of the Association'. Nevertheless in October 1926 Armstrongs made initial approaches regarding membership, eventually joining, but William Beardmore & Co never did enjoy membership of the LMA. A member of the LMA since its foundation fifty years earlier, Beyer, Peacock & Co withdrew in 1926 over a difference of opinion. Rules instituted in 1918 required members to submit details of all quotations given in response to enquiries; but as patentees BP saw no reason to oblige with regard to quotations for Garratts. Other members saw this differently as BP would on occasion offer a Garratt when others were obliged to submit

more conventional proposals. Under its forceful Chairman, Sir Sam Fay, the Beyer, Peacock board also claimed to see little value in continuing its membership. BP's subsequent estrangement from 'the brotherhood' doubtless facilitated NBL in it rather surreptitiously building ten 4-8-2 + 2-8-4 Garratts for the Kenya & Uganda Railway in 1931, thereby infringing Manchester-held patents. These Garratts were actually ordered by the Crown Agents for the Colonies, which would have provided drawings from the previous BP order, and who were therefore party to this rather dubious transaction.

Beyer, Peacock & Co was welcomed back into the LMA fold in June 1935, at the last of many meetings over many years to be presided over by the 'grand old man' of the British locomotive industry, Sir Hugh Reid, of NBL, who died just four weeks later. Also entering somewhat belatedly at this time was Armstrong Whitworth & Co, which in late 1934 had secured an order from the LMS for 100 Class 5 mixed traffic 4-6-0s.

In November 1935 a special meeting was convened to discuss further large locomotive orders which the LMS was about to place with private builders, primarily for members to reach mutual agreement as regards the minimum prices to be quoted in response. The types involved were Class 5 mixed traffic 4-6-0s, Class 8F heavy goods 2-8-0s and Class 4 2-6-4Ts. Somewhat surprisingly the Hunslet Engine Co expressed interest in building 2-6-4Ts and W G Bagnall Ltd some 2-8-0s.

In the event NBL secured the 2-6-4T order (for 69 engines) and Vulcan Foundry that for the 2-8-0s (73). One can only imagine the dismay in certain quarters when it became known that Armstrongs had landed the *entire* order for no fewer than 227 4-6-0s, a British record.

Delivery of the latter commenced in July 1936 and continued until December 1937 when Armstrong's withdrew entirely from locomotive building. Only 18 months after it had joined the LMA, the latter convened another Special Meeting in January 1937, at which by arrangement Armstrong's representatives were not present, to discuss a proposal which that firm had submitted for what was rather quaintly termed its 'sterilisation'. It had offered to withdraw from locomotive building for a period of twenty years on receipt of a payment of £150,000, with its goodwill, drawings, patterns and press blocks etc passing to the LMA. Coupled with the Government's desire to rationalise the locomotive industry it is almost certain that given the deteriorating situation in Europe as regards relations with Germany, there was also a hidden agenda here to restore the Scotswood plant to munitions manufacture, which indeed came to pass.

Between 1922 and 1938 there were a number of ambiguous references to contacts between the Locomotive Manufacturers Association and its German opposite number (the Lokomotiv Verbund) to try and establish some kind of mutual understanding. Germany had bounced back with a vengeance after 1918, exporting 1486 locomotives in 1921 and no less than 1890 in 1922 before experiencing difficult times and then building no more than the British industry in the mid and late 1920s. The moves appear to have been primarily initiated from the German side only to meet a strong measure of indifference on the part of the British. In 1926 an unidentified British member of the LMA had been accused of lending patterns to a German competitor which had secured a South African contract. In fact, between the wars German manufacturers built about twice as many locomotives for South Africa as did British, culminating in a particularly large order which was largely responsible for putting German

LMS Class 5 4-6-0 No 5241 of the second batch of these engines built by Armstrong Whitworth & Co during 1936-37. The excellent finish will be noted. *NRM DY 21354*

locomotive exports as a whole ahead of British for the first time in 1938. The high price of American-built locomotives after 1918 probably explains why the US industry had not been, after all, a serious competitor.

The Germans had an altogether more technical approach to steam locomotive design, but ten years earlier in November 1928 the LMA had received a letter from the Department of Scientific & Industrial Research regarding a proposed national Locomotive Experimental Station for joint use by the home railways and the private locomotive industry.

Matters progressed extremely slowly, a year later, by which time the world economy had collapsed, the locomotive industry was wary of contributing even the suggested *one quarter* of the estimated capital and maintenance costs (of £100,000 and £25,000). One can only sympathise, indeed during the next decade its output would be pitifully low with very little *to* test. The main line railways, of whom Sir Nigel Gresley, Chief Mechanical Engineer of the LNER, was the chief protagonist had much more to gain. He pointed out that even modest savings in fuel consumption through research would quickly recoup the cost of the proposed plant.

The LMA finally backed out of the project in May 1936, by which time the LMS and LNER boards had effectively agreed to go ahead alone together with a joint testing station at Rugby, which was served by one each of their respective main lines. Owing to the intervention of World War 2 the completion of the plant was greatly delayed and it was not inaugurated until late 1948.

During World War 2 the LMA was concerned with prioritising resources for the war effort once the industry had come back

into its own after mid-1942. By 1944 for example, at NBL where 'Austerity' 2-8-0s were being turned out in prodigious numbers, there was a conflict of interests regarding the simultaneous construction of 4-8-2s also ordered by the Ministry of Supply for South Africa where these were urgently needed. There was only so much steel and so many men to transform it.

As the war finally drew to a close, in early 1945 the LMA had discussions with the four British main line railways regarding the construction of a limited number of locomotives over a period of five years, which the railways had been unable to build in their own workshops during hostilities. The LNER and GWR duly placed quite substantial orders as previously indicated, and the LMA again made informal approaches in late 1950 to the now unified British Railways. The considered response from R A Riddles, dated 26 January 1951, indicated:

'Owing to restrictions in capital investment, and the better use of locomotives now existing, this showed that the demand for locomotives would not be even sufficient to utilise the full capacity of our own workshops, and it would appear that this condition would persist at least until 1955.'

Meanwhile, the LMA itself had recently, somewhat magnanimously, entered into a technical agreement which in the longer term would conflict with the interests of its members. The question of establishing a national locomotive building plant in India had been actively discussed since 1919 and was still very much to the fore in 1939. Deferred by the war and finally spurred by Indian Independence in 1947 the Chittaranjan Agreement was concluded in 1949 with the LMA. The first locomotive to be steamed off the plant in East Bengal in November 1950, a Class WG 2-8-2, was assembled *entirely* from British made components, but the proportion of imported components and materials steadily reduced over the coming years. However there would initially be a continuing need for India to import substantial numbers of steam locomotives. In late 1953 great dismay was expressed by the LMA when it discovered that India had placed orders overseas for over 400 locomotives, to be built in Germany, Austria and Japan. It appeared that lower quoted prices, and quicker delivery dates than could be confirmed by British builders due to pressure of existing orders, were the prime reasons. It was grimly noted that the large orders received by a German contractor were not unrelated to the extensive technical assistance it had provided to the Tata enterprise regarding locomotive building, but that similar recognition did not seem to have been accorded British builders with their century of service to the sub-continent *and* their recent assistance concerning the establishment of the Chittaranjan plant.

The implications for the British locomotive industry of the British Railways Modernisation Plan influencing motive power policy in Commonwealth countries was noted in 1955. Hard on its heels came the Clean Air Act, 1956. This almost killed the remaining domestic market for industrial steam locomotives. Even the National Coal Board had been making extensive purchases of diesels since 1947. However by the late 1950s a glut of coal was developing and the NCB began to review its motive power policy, especially as experiments were afoot (by the Hunslet Engine Company) to reduce or eliminate smoke emission. This was debated at the LMA's July 1959 meeting, which was the final occasion when steam locomotive matters were seriously discussed, as there was also concern as to the effects of the disposal to industry of redundant steam locomotives from British Railways now that the Modernisation Plan was rapidly gaining momentum.

This concern proved to be unfounded, (more serious would be the availability of almost new 0-6-0 diesels sold by BR to industry a decade later). In 1963 the LMA, latterly entitled the Locomotive & Allied Manufacturers Association, was re-styled the Railway Industry Association.

The LMA had originally come into being to prevent the home railway companies from building locomotives for other than their own use. The Transport Act, 1947, which legislated for the formation of British Railways on 1 January 1948, actually contained a clause which specifically precluded the new entity from manufacturing *anything* for other than its own use. In 1949 BR had unwittingly found itself potentially doing just that. Eight 2-6-4Ts were already on order at Derby Works, in succession to ten already built during 1946 - 47 for the Northern Counties Committee in Ulster, a subsidiary of the LMS (and earlier of the Midland Railway). The NCC had become incorporated in the new independent Ulster Transport Authority on 1 April 1949. Legal advice was sought and construction went ahead, ironically the LMA does not even appear to have debated this particular issue.

Ultimately in the post-steam construction era, legislation was passed in 1968 enabling British Railways workshops to compete for commercial contracts, although in practice this was only rarely invoked, mainly with regard to passenger rolling stock for Ireland.

TABLE 14 — Reported Workforce of British Locomotive Builders 1883-1911 (and 1950) from LMA Returns

	BUILDERS										
Year	BP	D	HE	K	MW	NW	N	NBL	SS	RS	VF
1883	1690	1850		808		300	2150		1042	800	690
1884	1820	1988		1165		450	2400		1008	838	691
1885	1708	1404	166	1043	278	397	2456		1024	425	583
1886 - 1887 Not available											
1888	1501	1400	257	1150	437	354	1772		1014	408	385
1889	1735	1744	286	1260	589	518	2166		1330	300	538
1890	2159	1960	263	1255	493	474	2505		1336	530	679
1891	1971	1940	282	1270	447	419	2584		165	659	666
1892	1292	1697	240	1268	267	377	2307		1507	455	561
1893	1359	1775	256	1079	293	320	1896		1246	344	486
1894	1239	1465	234	1143	236	349	1510		1145	320	610
1895	1196	1773	242	915	314	337	1617		1178	387	514
1896	1727	1868	245	1192	370	459	2360		1333	586	770
1897	1756	2004	271	1192	483	443	2600		1432	885	792
1898	1792	1931	270	1357	355	517	2937		1435	894	713
1899	1866	2017	300	1440	590	526	3275		1561	1047	820
1900 - 1904 Not available											
1905	2301		290	1410	350	458		7716		862	1325
1906	2622	-	350	1833	433	430	-	7837	-	1084	1535
1907	2638	-	353	1973	459	510	-	7999	-	1191	1698
1908	2789	-	323	1944	282	525	-	7192	-	965	1757
1909	2342	-	283	1680	290	485	-	7037	-	-	1801
1910	2349	-	300	1691	270	541	-	6216	-	-	1693
1911	2368	-	309	1612	245	706	-	7346	-	-	1701
										RSH	
1950	1600	-	650	-	-	-	-	4800	-	1450	2400

Prior to 1914 LMA members were levied according to the size of their workforce. After 1918 levies were made on a percentage of sales basis.

THE BRITISH LOCOMOTIVE INDUSTRY AT WORK

In 1996, in what could well prove to be the last instance of its kind, a major overseas railway administration issued a detailed specification for a highly specialised steam locomotive with the invitation to manufacturers to submit quotations. By its very nature there was only one serious contender (in Europe) but 18 months later there had been no positive outcome.

During the steam era proper there would usually be several keen competitors and a contract could be concluded within a fortnight. At the end of the day the customer's primary concern was How Much and How Soon? Success for the builder could depend on providing the lowest quotation and/or offering the earliest delivery time. Each of these factors could depend on the number of engines required.

In the simplest scenario, which applied to many of the orders placed by the larger British railway companies, the builders worked 'to drawings and specification supplied'. Nevertheless, even if this was a repeat order, there could still be detailed modifications and the contractor would be required to furnish a complete set of 'as made' drawings. This was the case with the LNER Class K3 three-cylinder 2-6-0s built by Armstrong Whitworth & Co, Robert Stephenson & Co, and the North British Locomotive Company. In the 19th century a greater measure of latitude was sometimes allowed, eg with the North Eastern Railway Class BTP 0-4-4WTs, whose detailed styling varied in detail according to builder.

Some British main line railway locomotive classes built after 1900 were designed *in detail* by the builder in accordance with a specification provided by the railway. This was certainly the case with 4-4-2, 4-6-0, 0-8-0, and 0-8-4T classes ascribed to J G Robinson on the Great Central between 1902 and 1907, and a number of designs on the Glasgow & South Western Railway, commencing with the Manson 4-6-0s of 1903, and culminating with the magnificent Whitelegg 4-6-4 tanks of 1922. Certainly some of the Peter Drummond classes were designed in outline only at Kilmarnock c 1912 - 13 for reasons which are now unclear.

Even after 1923, the newly formed London Midland & Scottish and London & North Eastern railways had urgent needs for three-cylinder 4-6-0s of entirely new design and both turned to the North British Locomotive Co with its extensive resources. Thus the 'Royal Scot' was produced (50 off) in a matter of months during 1927 under direct LMS supervision. It was followed by the Class B17 the following year for the Great Eastern

Section of the LNER with its stringent weight restrictions ('we to draw out' according to the NBL Order Book). Ironically, subsequent repeat orders for both went elsewhere, including both railways' own works.

In the case of smaller railways the builder had a virtually free hand provided it kept to prescribed weight and loading gauge limits. This was particularly the case with the so-called Cumming 4-4-0s and 4-6-0s on the Highland Railway, delivered by R & W Hawthorn Leslie & Co of Newcastle-upon-Tyne between 1916 and 1921, which followed hard on the heels of an earlier 4-6-0 design which had offended the civil engineer on both counts in late 1915.

Alternatively the railway might issue a detailed specification and yet be prepared to accept a completely different alternative from it provided this fulfilled the essential requirements. Thus the specification issued by the Furness Railway in November 1918 for six inside-cylinder 4-6-4Ts contained a clause which stated:

'contractors have the option of submitting alternative designs embodying the principal dimensions shown on the drawing'. The North British Locomotive Company (unsuccessfully) offered a modified version of the 4-6-2T which it had built in 1917 to Caledonian Railway order. Kitson & Co's successful submission included a number of relatively minor changes, including some to the boiler whose outer shell was to become identical with that of the Great Central 2-8-0, of which many had already been built in Leeds and for which the press blocks were already to hand.

A specification also would list the materials to be used and identified approved suppliers of these. It was standard practice for a specification to make no reference to weights, although maximum or minimum permitted axleload might sometimes be indicated. In addition to quoting a price and delivery time, a builder was required to calculate the weight *in full working order* and its distribution and keep to this within something of the order of $\pm 2\frac{1}{2}$ per cent in the event of receiving the order. In practice this was not always actually achieved (see Chapter 9).

Very often working 'to drawings and specification', leaving little scope to exercise their own skill, the builders really came into their own with overseas contracts. Here the customer would lay down requirements without indicating in any way the actual form of locomotive required. Details would be provided of rail gauge, loading gauge, axle weight restrictions, weight of rail,

The term mass production could hardly be applied to the British locomotive industry, but it was on rare occasions approached by the North British Locomotive Company with big 100-engine orders from India and South Africa. Here are several units of the most successful Indian 'X' series standards, the Class XD 2-8-2, under construction in May 1946 at the Queens Park Works of NBL which was completing an order for 60 such engines, while the Hyde Park Works were busy with 50 similar engines, all ordered in 1944.

track curvature and ruling gradient, train weight and operating speed. Also to be taken into account would be the type and calorific value of available fuel, and climatic conditions. Such enquiries could produce a diverse range of submissions from different builders. A rare such insight concerned the privately owned standard gauge heavily graded Wolgan Valley Railway in New South Wales, which was published in *Engineering* for 14 April 1911. This provided the basic, but regrettably by no means consistent details, of submissions from five leading British and American builders for different types of articulated locomotives which they then espoused.

Kitson & Co	Meyer type	113 tons (with tender)
North British Loco Co	Fairlie type	73 tons
Beyer, Peacock & Co	Garratt type	(weight not given)
Baldwin Loco Works	Mallet type	90 tons
Lima Locomotive Works	Shay type	70 tons

The heaviest contender was the Kitson proposal, but the lightest, the geared 70 ton Shay from Lima in the USA, won the day with three being ordered, later followed by a more powerful version weighing 90 tons.

Even for the domestic market the diversity could be surprising. In 1913 the Metropolitan Railway put out an enquiry for a tank engine to work its outer residential services between Harrow and Aylesbury. Beyer, Peacock & Co offered a four-cylinder 4-6-4T, and North British an 0-8-4T, but the little Yorkshire Engine Company of Sheffield 'won' with a relatively compact 0-6-4T. A few years later when the Met enquired for 4-4-4Ts, NBL offered to build North Eastern Railway type three-cylinder 4-4-4Ts provided it could obtain the necessary drawings, but Kerr Stuart & Co received the order, another triumph for a small builder.

There was no copyright on locomotive designs, for in 1922, when responding to an enquiry from Romania NBL submitted a scheme for a Somerset & Dorset 2-8-0 modified for oil burning and provided with a cow catcher. By no means all NBL 'project

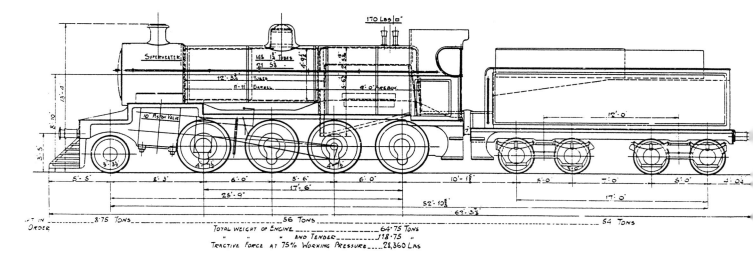

An NBL 'project sketch' produced in May 1922 for a heavy goods engine for Romania. It is actually a 2-8-0 built by the Midland Railway at Derby Works in 1914 for the Somerset & Dorset Joint Railway, but given a 'cow catcher' and large bogie tender incorporating oil tanks for oil firing.

sketches' now survive. A register of these covering the period 1900 - 1924 contains such tantalising entries as a 2-12-0 for New South Wales (1913) and a four-cylinder 2-10-4T for the Great Indian Peninsula Railway (1916).

Beyer, Peacock & Co made a large number of Garratt schemes between about 1912 and 1958, only a minute fraction of which came to fruition. In 1946 when it was comfortably loaded with orders (which it had not been in 1936, and would not be in 1956) BP could afford to respond somewhat tersely to the Victorian Railways concerning a proposed 4-6-2 + 2-6-4 Garratt that 'it had spent a considerable sum over the past 20 years in supplying similar line-drawings and quotations for Australian Railways without much return'. It also indicated that it

would not be prepared to undertake an order for less than five engines, and would prefer at least ten, with major spares, eg boilers, to be built concurrently. On the other hand the VR had also enquired whether complete drawings could be made for *Australian* manufacture! No order ensued, but BP later tried to interest the newly formed British Railways with a rather similar design in 1949 for service in Scotland between Perth and Inverness, but without success.

The preliminary design process involved the tedious matter of weight estimation. Where possible, reference would be made to an already established comparable design for which detailed component weights were available, which could be used as a basis and scaled up or down, as appropriate. In late 1950 Vulcan Foundry did some detailed calculations for a powerful standard gauge 2-10-2 for Greece and as a yardstick used the newly de-

A rather strange 4-6-0 passenger engine derived from the 2-8-0 above. Despite high hopes by British builders of securing large orders from Romania, these actually went to Germany, which supplied Prussian type 0-10-0s etc.

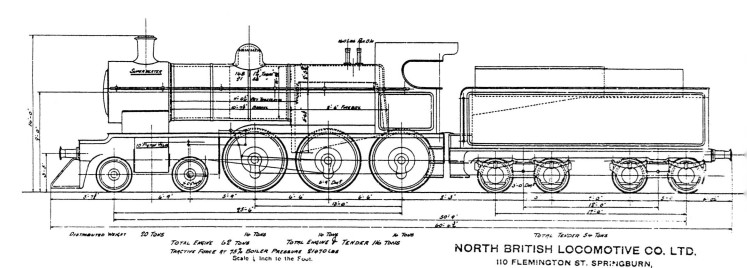

NORTH BRITISH LOCOMOTIVE CO. LTD.
110 FLEMINGTON ST. SPRINGBURN,

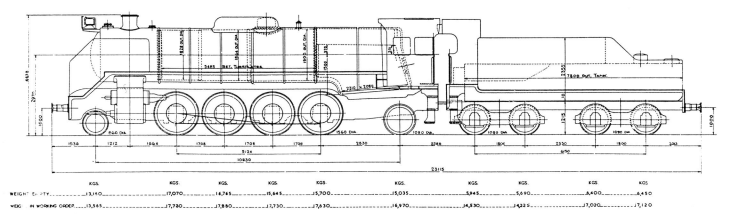

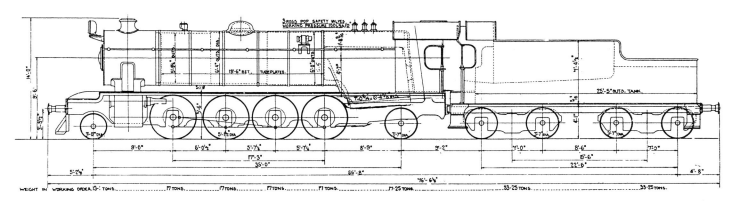

The last significant British steam locomotive export order for continental Europe comprised 25 2-8-2s plus 100 sets of parts by NBL
for the 5ft 6in gauge RENFE in Spain in 1953 (upper). This was
developed from the long established Indian 'XD' design built, mainly by NBL, between 1926 and 1948 (lower). Although by no means
identical the similarities are unmistakeable.

---

signed 2-10-2 for Iran then in production. Four options were
examined:

1. 'Small' boiler, steel firebox, no stoker etc,
   (estimated weight)   118.4 tons
2. 'Small' boiler, copper firebox, stoker, feed pump,
   double chimney,   122.2 tons
3. 'Large' boiler, steel firebox, no stoker etc,   127.2 tons
4. 'Large' boiler, copper firebox, stoker etc,   131.2 tons

In the event, owing to a 1949 post-war reparations treaty the engines were later built in Italy (and were notably unsuccessful).

Having produced a scheme which satisfied the customer and
resulted in a firm order, working drawings would then be developed. The earliest would often be 'ordering sketches' giving extreme dimensions so that frame plates, copper firebox plates, and
axles etc could be indented for. Drawings were initially drafted in
pencil, checked, and then traced onto linen ('cloth') and inked
in. Prior to 1914 many contact builders coloured their drawings,
yellow for brass, orange for copper, grey for cast iron, dark blue
for steel etc. As a result the overall general arrangement drawing
could be a work of art. Such were the increases in labour costs
that after about 1918 drawings were rarely coloured. Similarly

from the 1930s general arrangement drawings were no longer *de
rigeur*, being considered a decidedly expensive academic nicety.
(Their prime function was to confirm that everything fitted together).

It was not a question of producing all the drawings, about
100 - 150 pre 1914, and perhaps 600 by the 1950s, before active construction commenced. At busy times the drawing office
might only be 2 - 3 days ahead of the shops. The latter worked
from paper prints made by photo-chemical means from the
translucent tracings, which were highly durable and could be
amended if necessary. A set would be filed in the drawing office,
and another set supplied to the customer. It was a very labour intensive process, which nevertheless lasted to the end of the steam
era and was by no means confined to the locomotive industry.

The design process accounted for a relatively small proportion of the building cost, around 1914 a set of drawings for a 4-
4-0 was quoted at £125 and for a 4-6-0 £200. More expensive
was the production of new jigs, patterns and templates. Both private and railway drawing offices tried to utilise those already to
hand where possible, but hopefully not to the extent of compro-
mising the overall design. The fabrication of new cylinder patterns and press blocks for boiler making was a major item. (A
celebrated alleged instance of parsimony in the latter regard concerned the London & North Western Railway 'Claughton' class
four-cylinder 4-6-0, first built at Crewe Works in 1913, which
preserved the same boiler diameter of preceding smaller inside-
cylinder 4-4-0 and 4-6-0 designs to the detriment of its own performance). In reality the construction of very small numbers of
locomotives at a time for minor railways must have been very
uneconomic for all concerned. Because of this it was by no

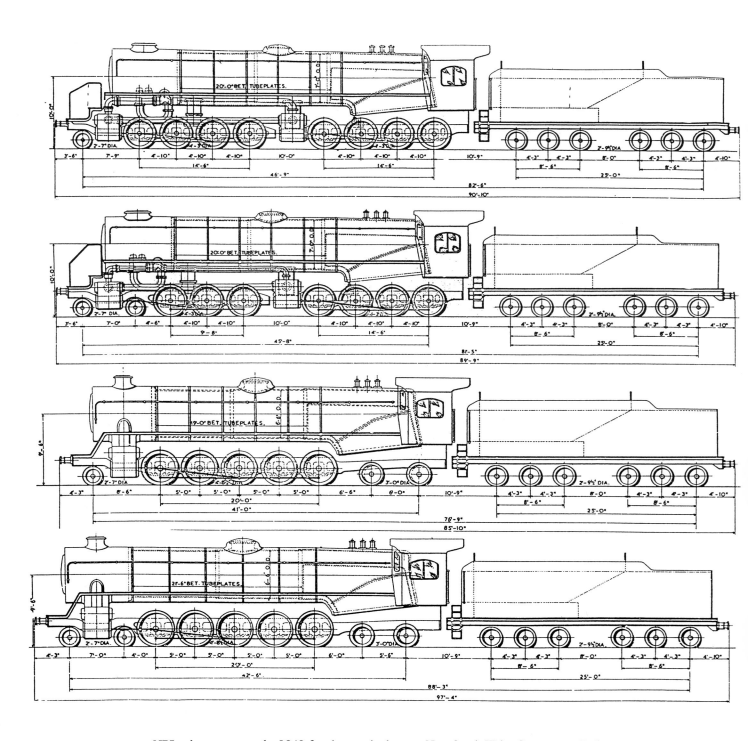

NBL schemes prepared c.1948 for the standard gauge New South Wales Government Railways, for two-cylinder 2-10-4 and 4-10-4, and four-cylinder simple expansion 4-6-8-0 and 2-8-8-0 Mallet articulateds. All have the same grate area of 62.5 ft² and axleload of 15½ tons, very similar in this respect to the AD60 4-8-4 + 4-8-4 Garratt successfully put forward by Beyer, Peacock & Co around the same time.

The largest cylinders ever cast in Britain were 31½ in diameter x 26 in stroke low pressure cylinders for two cylinder compound 4-8-0s (NBL), 2-8-2s (BP & RS) and 4-8-4Ts (AW) built for the Central Argentine Railway during the 1920s. Here is a newly finished cylinder (most probably cast by Kitson & Co) at Scotswood Works, Newcastle, for one of the twenty 4-8-4Ts built there in 1928. Its weight which was actually less than that of the smaller high pressure cylinder was specified with quite remarkable precision in the builder's weight schedule.

CENTRAL ARGENTINE RAILWAY.

20 TANK LOCOMOTIVES CLASS M.S. 6A.

REQN. No. 2383.   TYPE 4-8-4.   SPEC'N. No. V137.

LIST OF DETAILED WEIGHTS.

Drg. No. Section	Item	Quantity	Description	Material	T.	C.	Q.	L.	Oz.
91 B25	22	1	Handgrip on Smokebox.	Steel	-	-	-	4	8
" CB	231-234	1Set	Motion Footsteps Complete.	"	-	1	3	-	-
92 H2	90	1 Including H2/16.	H.P.Cylinder.	C.I.	1	14	2	25	8
93 H2	81	1 Including H2/17.	L.P.Cylinder.	"	1	13	1	10	-
		1	L.P.Cover.	"	-	4	1	27	-
		1	Lagging Plate.	Steel	-	-	-	25	12
		1	Casing over Cylinder Cover.	"	-	-	1	21	12
		1 1	L.P.Piston) Bearing Ring)	S.C.) G.M.)	-	4	1	6	4
		3	Rings.	C.I.	-	-	-	22	12

A weight diagram for these remarkable locomotives, which showed unmistakeable Derby influence around the cab (several senior CAR officers had earlier served on the Midland Railway).

---

means unusual to find locomotives of precisely the same design on two different railways, eg 0-6-2Ts on the Lancashire, Derbyshire & East Coast and Rhondda & Swansea Bay railways from Kitson & Co built between 1895 and 1904. Similarly two 0-6-0s built in 1921 for the Maryport & Carlisle Railway by the Yorkshire Engine Co 'under the skin' simply replicated the Hull & Barnsley Railway Class L of which the same builder had produced a small batch of five in 1914, and with a dome added.

Cost was a prime concern to both parties. The prices calculated by different contractors to build the same locomotive have only comparatively rarely been recorded. An interesting example concerns the Great North of Scotland Railway Class T 4-4-0 for which bids were taken in mid-1895 and again in late 1896. Although the value of the pound sterling was virtually constant

The Scotswood boiler shop of Armstrong Whitworth & Co in the mid-1920s showing boilers under construction for the South Australian Railways 4-6-2, 2-8-2 and 4-8-2 locomotives.

NRM 1143/82

pre-1914, commodity prices could vary considerably according to demand. As a result building costs could change significantly within a short period:

	mid-1895 (14 engines)	late-1896 (12 engines)
R Stephenson & Co	£2590	£3430
Beyer, Peacock & Co	£2550	£3200
Kitson & Co	£2425	£2930
Vulcan Foundry Ltd	£2300	£3000
Dübs & Co	£2360	£2925
Sharp, Stewart & Co	£2250	£2850
Neilson & Co	£2245	£2975
Average	£2389	£3044

The 1896 quotations showed an average 27 per cent increase over those for 1895. It came down to supply and demand, during 1896 the seven builders collectively produced over 700 engines, compared to about 400 in 1895, a sign of the rapidly

improving economy. Neilson & Co was awarded the order on both occasions, although not submitting the lowest tender in 1896 it could offer earlier delivery than Sharp Stewart probably because it already had the patterns.

During the 1919 - 21 period material prices and wages increased very rapidly making life very difficult for builders which before 1914 had worked to fixed price contracts. Complex price variation agreements had therefore to be made with customers to protect the builders' legitimate interests. Even so several contracts executed around 1922 in particular incurred a financial loss for the contractors, eg the special 'Oban' 4-6-0s for the Caledonian Railway by NBL, which charged only £5211 apiece although actually costing £6812 each to build.

Delivery times typically ranged between 6 and 18 months depending upon the state of the builder's order book. Agreed delivery schedules were frequently not met in practice even when there was little pressure. In January 1935 NBL received an order from the LNER for 20 Class K3 2-6-0s which the railway could probably have built for itself. The first engine was to be delivered in 20 weeks time with the remainder following at a rate of two per week. In fact the first engine was handed over on the very day the last should have been delivered!

When locomotives were required urgently a penalty clause was often incorporated in the contract permitting the purchaser to deduct so much per engine per week delay from the original

The Erecting Shop of R & W Hawthorn Leslie & Co, less than one mile away a few years earlier showing two superheater goods 4-6-0s for the Highland Railway.

agreed cost. This might well be waived if the circumstances were indeed beyond the contractor's control. Sometimes payment was only made after completion of a specified trouble free mileage of 1,000 or 2,000 miles. Alternatively payment was also made in three instalments. The first after the steaming trial, the second on delivery, and the balance on completion of a satisfactory specified mileage. This was variously split, eg 50/25/25, or 60/30/10 per cent of the total invoiced cost.

Having received a firm order, the builder would then order steel plate and non-ferrous materials from specialist suppliers. Major castings such as cylinders and wheel centres might well be bought in from foundries specialising in such work, although Beyer, Peacock & Co was unusual in possessing its own steel foundry. It is on record that in 1928 when undertaking an urgent order for 50 0-6-2Ts for the Great Western Railway, Armstrong Whitworth & Co experienced considerable difficulty making the cylinder castings and resorted to Kitson & Co, which was proficient in this field. A host of special components, eg water, steam pressure and vacuum gauges, injectors, ejectors, whistles, safety valves and lubricators would have to be ordered from enterprises, which tended to be located in the North of England. After about 1920, particular collaboration would be required with The Superheater Company, of Trafford Park, Manchester. Superheater header castings were particularly intricate, especially those which incorporated multiple regulator valves.

During construction the Locomotive Superintendent or his representative was entitled to inspect the locomotives at any time, and reject inferior workmanship or materials. In the case of locomotives for colonial railways the Crown Agents undertook this demanding task, or for railways in India London-based consulting engineers. A succinct account of the diplomatic art of locomotive inspection by one with considerable experience of this work is reproduced as Appendix 1.

On near completion steam trials of a necessarily restricted nature would take place in the works yard, there was not a great deal of room in which to manoeuvre a 4-8-4 + 4-8-4 Garratt at the Gorton Foundry. Most builders had multi-gauge tracks ranging from 2ft to 5ft 6in.

Weighing would also take place, both to provide a check on the original design estimate and to adjust individual axleloads. Although two locomotives might be built to the same drawings, weightwise they could come out quite differently. In 1916 the Great Northern Railway at Doncaster Works built ten 2-6-0s. Although *average* weight was 64.35 tons in working order, *actual* weights varied between 63.8 and 65.1 tons. Although the final two engines both weighed 64.5 tons, one had a maximum axleload of 18.0 and the other 19.0 tons.

A virtually complete Class 15F 4-8-2 is bodily lifted along the Erecting Shop at NBL, soon after World War 2.

Engines were initially finished in matt grey primer which, picked out with black and white lining served as the basis for a series of official photographs. Some of the earliest photographs of an industrial nature were of new engines at Beyer, Peacock & Co in the late 1850s, by James Mudd of Manchester. This practice, which often included painting out extraneous background detail on the glass plate negative, was commonly followed to the end of the steam era a century later. Some Indian contracts specifically required a 6ft tall man, usually replete with bowler hat, to stand beside the engine.

Engines built for the home railways were usually despatched 'dead' with motion dismantled, in the formation of an ordinary

scheduled goods train, eg the Furness 4-6-4Ts. There were also instances of new locomotives travelling under their own steam, eg the two 0-6-0s for the Maryport & Carlisle Railway over the Midland Railway from Sheffield to Carlisle in 1921.

Prior to the 1920s locomotives destined for overseas, of necessity were despatched in dismantled form and erected on arrival by the builder's fitters. A major development c 1924 was the advent of the purpose-built 'Belships' on the Norwegian-owned Christen Smith line. These were provided with their own craneage to lift complete locomotives onto the deck on which a surprisingly large number could be accommodated abreast across the beam.

As it happened, most British builders of large locomotives were located relatively close to a major coastal port, with the notable exception of Kitson & Co of Leeds, which nevertheless in 1924 despatched large 4-6-2s and 2-8-2s to India, where about one *third* of its total production was destined. Nearly twenty years earlier an exceptionally large 2-10-0 built by Robert Stephenson & Co in Darlington for Argentina was sent by rail to Liverpool, for which it was reported at the time that 'special arrangements' had to be made.

A Class WG 2-8-2 for India under close inspection at NBL, c.1950.

Two brand new 'King Arthur' 4-6-0s for the Southern Railway are towed south from their Glasgow birthplace by an ex-North British Railway 0-6-0 in 1926.

P Ransome Wallis Collection, NRM (PRW 616)

On arrival in foreign parts trials would be undertaken before an engine entered regular traffic, on completion of which final payment to the builder would be made.

Rarely is it now possible to provide a detailed chronology concerning a specific locomotive order, but such can be reconstructed from diverse sources, for the New South Wales Government Railways Class AD60 4-8-4 + 4-8-4 Beyer Garratt No 6002. (Although this was the second engine in the class, it was the first *actually* to enter traffic):

1 February 1949 — Initial scheme prepared by Beyer, Peacock & Co
21 September 1949 — 25 engines ordered at total cost of £1,488,937.50 (25 more engines were ordered in August 1950)
Late 1949-late 1951 — Detail design and fabrication of major parts. Cast steel engine beds ordered from and made in USA
20 March 1952 — Boiler steam test
16 April 1952 — Engine steam test
Late April 1952 — Engine dismantled
5 May 1952 — Boiler unit despatched by road, and engine units sent by rail to Liverpool Docks
13 June 1952 — With No 6001 arrived at Sydney, unloaded 5 days later
Late June/early July 1952 — Assembled and painted at Eveleigh Shops, Sydney
30 July 1952 — Initial trial trip, (light engine)
1 August 1952 — Entered revenue earning service

A Beyer, Peacock representative travelled out with Nos 6001/2 and supervised their assembly and initial trials, after which he returned to England.

The unusually long four years which elapsed between initial enquiry and the beginning of fleet operation corresponded with a critical period. In 1948 the planning of a new sizeable batch of steam locomotives was still routine and would have gone largely unquestioned almost anywhere outside the United States. There, by late 1952 the diesel electric locomotive had gained the upper hand and its manufacturers were already seeking potential markets further afield. This included Australia, where the NSWGR had experimented successfully with trial units in 1951, ie *before* the arrival of the first 4-8-4 + 4-8-4, whose *début* was not greeted with universal enthusiasm. Of the 50 engines ordered only 42 were assembled, one of which was retired as early as February 1955, almost two years before the final engine entered traffic.

In addition to producing complete locomotives the manufacturers also derived significant revenue from supplying spares, from split pins to complete boilers. This often helped to keep them in business during periods of industrial depression. Interestingly a particular builder might receive an order regardless of whether or not it had previously supplied the locomotive in question. (This was possible due to the practice of the original builder providing 'as made' tracings with the order). This particularly applied to boilers, for example in 1917 Vulcan Foundry made three spare boilers for the ten 0-6-4Ts which Hawthorn Leslie had built only three years earlier for the Barry Railway. In its turn during this period Hawthorns made two boilers for North British Railway 4-4-2s, although it had not built any of these magnificent locomotives. In such instances flanging of the plates was probably sub-contracted to the original builder and therefore owner of the press blocks. In the case of the NBR 4-4-2 boilers Robert Stephenson & Co doubtless assisted as it had both built some of the engines and several later spares. Examination of Hawthorn's surviving drawing registers indicates that the latter worked both to 'drawings received' and also made some new ones, probably reflecting the enforced resort to iron and steel inner fireboxes on account of the acute wartime shortage of copper. Rival locomotive builders often did business with each other in this way. Stephenson's and Hawthorn's are known

Two standard 4-6-2s for India are conveyed from the Vulcan Foundry to the docks on special LMS wagons designed for the purpose. Such movements were often made on a Sunday.

I Fisher Collection

A brand new 2-10-0 for Turkey is edged with extreme care under the Liverpool & Manchester line outside the Vulcan Foundry while en route by road to the docks for shipment. Clearances amounted to virtually a fraction of an inch.

I Fisher Collection

Over a year after it was built, the diplomatic crisis over, a 2-10-2 for Iran is finally embarked at Birkenhead in 1954.   *I Fisher Collection*

to have directly co-operated when still located 'next door' to each other in Newcastle in the 19th century. Sharp Stewart & Co even ordered two 0-4-0 crane tank locomotives from Andrew Barclay & Co to act as works shunters in Glasgow. The second, delivered in 1902, lasted until the demise of NBL 60 years later. Dübs and Neilson's on the other hand each built their own, but in 1917 the largest traded with the smallest when North British obtained a stock 0-4-0ST from Peckett's!

During the 1920s and 1930s in particular, in addition to placing locomotive orders 'outside', in order to alleviate the domestic unemployment situation, orders for new boilers were similarly awarded, sometimes for incorporation in new locomotives being built in railway workshops. In the case of ten boilers ordered by the Southern Railway in early World War 2 from NBL for its new 'Merchant Navy' 4-6-2s, the builder contributed to the actual *design*, not least because of the novel employment of welded construction. However, not all their boilers were ordered from locomotive manufacturers.

TABLE 15 — Outside Contracts for Locomotive Boilers by 'Big Four' Railway Companies 1923-1947

1. London Midland & Scottish Railway (Western Division)

Date ordered:	Qty		
March 1924	50	for G2 0-8-0,	Vulcan Foundry
March 1924	20	for 'George V' 4-4-0,	Vickers Ltd
March 1924	50	for 'Prince' 4-6-0,	Vickers Ltd
March 1924	30	for '18 inch' 0-6-0,	Kerr Stuart & Co
March 1924	50	for 'Coal' 0-6-0,	Beyer, Peacock & Co
March 1924	50	for 'Coal' 0-6-0,	Ruston & Hornsby
May 1925	10	for 'Coal' 0-6-0,	Ruston & Hornsby
May 1925	20	for 2-4-0/2-4-2T,	Ruston & Hornsby
May 1925	10	for '19 inch' 4-6-0,	Vulcan Foundry
May 1925	10	for 'Experiment' 4-6-0,	Vickers Ltd

2. Great Western Railway

Date ordered:	Qty		
December 1923	20	Std. No 10 (taper),	Vulcan Foundry
December 1923	20	Std. No 10 (taper),	Yorkshire Engine Co
October 1924	50	for '2301' 0-6-0,	Kerr Stuart & Co
January 1925	10	for '517' 0-4-2T,	Kitson & Co
January 1925	20	Std. No 2 (taper),	Kitson & Co
March 1925	60	Std. No 4 (taper),	Ruston & Hornsby
March 1925	10	for '850' 0-6-0PT,	Ruston & Hornsby
March 1925	10	Std. No 3 (taper),	Ruston & Hornsby
March 1925	20	Std. No 1 (taper),	Ruston & Hornsby

3. London & North Eastern Railway

Date ordered:	Qty		
1928 - 29	30	for Class J71/J72 0-6-0T,	Hawthorn Leslie & Co
1929 - 31	15	for Class J71/J72 0-6-0T,	Hawthorn Leslie & Co
1930	10	for Class B13 4-6-0/ Class Q6 0-8-0,	Hawthorn Leslie & Co
1930	12	for Class B17 4-6-0*,	Armstrong Whitworth & Co
1930	10	for Class G5 0-4-4T,	Kitson & Co
1930	9	for Class K3 2-6-0*,	N.B. Loco Co.
1930 - 31	5	for Class H1 4-4-4T,	N.B. Loco Co.
1931	15	for Class B17 4-6-0*,	Armstrong Whitworth & Co
1930 - 31	20	for Class J39 0-6-0*,	Robert Stephenson & Co
1931 - 32	14	for Class J72 0-6-0,	Hawthorn Leslie & Co
1932 - 33	15	for Class D49 4-4-0*/ Class J39 0-6-0*,	Robert Stephenson & Co
1946	10	for Class J37 0-6-0	Hunslet Engine Co
1950	10	for Class K3 2-6-0	Vulcan Foundry

4. Southern Railway

Date built:	Qty		
1940 - 41	10	for Class MN 4-6-2*,	N.B. Loco Co
1945	6	for Class N 2-6-0,	Kitson & Co
1946 - 47	12	for Class WC 4-6-2*,	N.B. Loco Co
1947 - 48	12	for Class S15/N15 4-6-0,	N.B. Loco Co

* for new engines built in railway works

Also during World War 2 the Southern Railway ordered the cylinder castings for its 40 Class Q1 0-6-0s, likewise being built in its own workshops, from the Vulcan Foundry, at the princely sum of £240 apiece. Towards the end of the war the Southern similarly ordered the cylinders for its first batch of 'West Country' 4-6-2s from Kitson & Co, the execution of which must have been one of the latter's last acts before its final demise in 1945.

Even after they had ceased complete steam locomotive construction, both Vulcan Foundry and Robert Stephenson & Hawthorns for some years manufactured the bar frames for new WG 2-8-2s being built in India by the Chittaranjan Locomotive Works, the latter as late as 1962.

A surprising order received from India in June 1960 by the Hunslet Engine Company was for a new boiler for one of the two 106 ton 2-10-2 tank engines built by Nasmyth Wilson & Co in 1922 for the Bombay Port Trust. The plates for this were flanged in Glasgow by NBL, and the boiler itself, which was considerably larger than anything which had previously been tackled by Hunslet, was assembled in Leeds, from where it was despatched in January 1962.

The smallest of the industrial locomotive builders, Peckett & Sons of Bristol, operated a highly organised 'immediate spare parts delivery service', recognising the great dependency of its smaller customers on the availability of their locomotives, which often received minimal if not non-existent maintenance. For many years the Peckett sales catalogues proclaimed:

"Specialisation and standardisation, the advantage of which has only lately been generally recognised, have been for years a distinctive feature of our productions.

By reason of the simplicity of construction and excellence of workmanship and materials the engines will not easily get out of order..... Being built to standard designs and templates, worn parts can always be replaced at the shortest notice by duplicates which will fit with the utmost accuracy in place of the originals.

We have most of the engines described in stock, and have others in an advanced state of completion and can always give quick delivery....Every engine passes the most rigid inspection during building, and on completion is thoroughly tested under steam on a special railroad of various gauges and different gradients we have specially laid down for the purpose.

When a single locomotive is depended upon, and where the stoppage of the locomotive may involve a shut-down and the idleness of a large number of men, our having a large stock of duplicate parts at hand is of great importance to our customers. We send any (specified) parts off the same day as the Order is received."

The marvel is, with hindsight, that so many locomotive builders remained in business for so long, especially after 1930. Rarely, if ever, had it been a particularly lucrative industry. To have worked in it was not always a particularly enjoyable experience either, at least on the testimony of two men who went on to greater things in quite different spheres. John (later Lord) Reith, the creator of the BBC, served a five year apprenticeship at the Hyde Park Works of the North British Locomotive Company between 1908 and 1913. Of his time at Britain's largest locomotive builder in its undoubted heyday he would later shudder at the recollection of the 'ghastly hours and squalid conditions'. At the

Beyer, Peacock & Co, early 1940s

BEYER PEACOCK LOCOMOTIVES

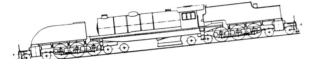

Beyer - Garratt Locomotives may represent the solution to your operating problems.

Have you
Single Line
Light Rail
Heavy Grades
Intensive Traffic

Then you should consider the use of Beyer-Garratts, which increase line capacity by hauling heavier loads and, at the same time, considerably reduce operating costs.

BEYER, PEACOCK & CO. LTD.
MANCHESTER

Locomotive Engineers

Est. 1854

LONDON OFFICE :
Telephone - - - Abbey 6295
Telegrams - - - Folgore, Sowest

MANCHESTER :
- - - East 1066
Telephone - -
Telegrams - - Loco, Gorton

LOCOMOTIVES
of all kinds and for all purposes!

"PARAGON"
Thermo - Electric
Locomotives and
Rail Cars.

Designed and Constructed for any Gauge of Railway and Conditions of Service at Home and Abroad. Save costly Power Stations and Maintenance Charges by the adaptation of independent Units. Can be designed to run on any fuel. Crude Oil, Petrol, Kerosene, Alcohol, Astatki, Suction or Town Gas. Eliminates boiler troubles and solves the Feed - water problem.

R. & W. HAWTHORN LESLIE & CO., LTD.,
Newcastle-upon-Tyne.
London Office :—54, Victoria Street, S.W.1.

R & W Hawthorn Leslie & Co, 1920s

other end of the scale during the same period, R J Mitchell, who would later design the 'Spitfire' fighter aircraft, was serving his time with Kerr Stuart & Co. Similarly his own published recollections were less than complimentary, but both no doubt simply reflected the harsh reality of life in British heavy industry at that time. By the 1950s, perhaps, working conditions would have somewhat improved with greater awarness of staff welfare, etc, particularly at the Vulcan Foundry which had adjoining sports facilities. It is known that some workers there stayed because they enjoyed the work, even though they could have received better remuneration elsewhere in the same area. There too was a genuine sense of regret when it all came to an end.

South African Railways
4-8-2 TYPE CLASS 15-E
LOCOMOTIVE

Office 20, Grosvenor Gardens, S.W.I.
: Sloane 8111/2.
: "Fossicker," Sowest, London.

ROBERT STEPHENSON & CO. LTD.
ESTABLISHED 1823

TELEPHONE: DARLINGTON 2700.   TELEGRAMS: "ROCKET," DARLINGTON.

Robert Stephenson & Co, mid-1930s

Contemporary promotional material by
British locomotive builders

for the Railways of the World

Steam . . . diesel hydraulic . . .
diesel electric . . . or electric . . .
in almost every country of the
world these locomotives built
by North British in Glasgow are
more than pulling their weight.
The service they provide is
ample evidence of the jealously
guarded reputation held by us
. . . a guarantee of even finer
locomotives to be developed
and built in the future.

STEAM

DIESEL-ELECTRIC

DIESEL-HYDRAULIC

ELECTRIC

NORTH BRITISH

NORTH BRITISH LOCOMOTIVE CO. LTD. GLASGOW

North British Locomotive Co, 1950s

GIVING RELIABLE SERVICE
ON FAMOUS LOCOMOTIVES
IN ALL PARTS OF THE WORLD

Illustrated here are
outstanding examples
recently fitted . . . .
L.N.E.R. Empress of
India and (below)
L.M.S. Coronation Scot

Exhaust Steam

INJECTORS

The only practical and
successful feedwater
heater for Locomotives.
10% Economy in fuel.
Used all over the world.
Over 30,000 Locomotives fitted.

DAVIES & METCALFE LTD.

ENGLAND

Power in hand –

MeLeSCo

SUPERHEATERS
means more power from steam

The SUPERHEATER *Company Ltd*

the authority on Superheated Steam

53 HAYMARKET . LONDON S.W.
Works TRAFFORD PARK, MANCHESTER 17

The Superheater Company, showing the
'modern engraving' style
fashionable in the early 1950s.

Component manufacturers
also advertised extensively
often illustrating a recent
exponent of their wares:-

One of the
70 'R' CLASS LOCOMOTIVES
built by *North British Locomotive Co., Ltd.*
for Victorian Government Railways

All 70 are
equipped throughout on all driving and carrying axles
with

SKF
SPHERICAL ROLLER BEARING
AXLEBOXES

The Skefko
Ball Bearing Co

THE SKEFKO BALL BEARING CO. LTD., LUTON

SPECIAL LOCOMOTIVES

Over the years a number of highly specialised locomotives, often articulated, were built by the British locomotive industry.

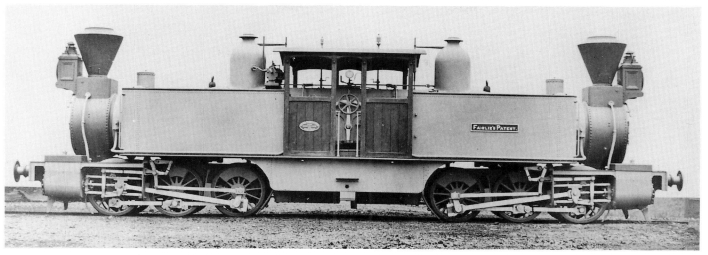

The first break away from the conventional rigid frame locomotive was the Double Fairlie in the 1870s. This virtually amounted to two locomotives back to back, (the Avonside Engine Company even allocated *two* works numbers to each engine!). This example was built by the Yorkshire Engine Company for the Poti & Tiflis Railway in Russia in 1874.   *(NRM 2174/86)*

A speciality of Kitson & Co was the Kitson Meyer, many of which were built for South America. This 0-8-6-0T rack and adhesion example was photographed amid the snow of the high Andes on the Argentine Transandine Railway about one year after it was built in Leeds in 1909.

P C Dewhurst Collection, NRM (NRM 189/92)

The most successful deviation from the conventional steam locomotive was the Beyer Garratt, which combined high power with modest axleload and considerable flexibility, which was well nigh impossible to achieve with a rigid frame design.

"Super-Garratt" Locomotive, 4' 8½" Gauge.   Beyer, Peacock & Co. Ltd.   Patent No. 230,888.

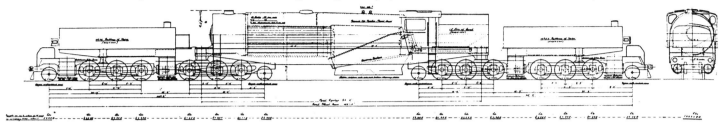

Gauge of Rails	4' 8½"	
Heating Surface :—Tubes ..	6,897 sq. feet	
Firebox ..	490 "	
Arch Tubes	95 "	
	7,482 "	
Superheater	1,818 "	(inside)
Total ..	9,300 "	

Grate Area 160 sq. ft.
Tractive Power 1,087 lb. per 1 lb. M.E.P. in the cylinders.
Tractive Force at 90% boiler pressure = 215,200 lb.
  „   „   75%   „   „   = 179,340 lb.
Ratio of Tractive Force (90%) to Adhesive Weight (Tanks Full) = 1 to 3·75.
  „   „   „   (75%)   „   „   „   „   = 1 to 4·5.
Total Water Capacity, 19,200 gallons. (American).

As early as 1927, *possibly* tongue in cheek, Beyer, Peacock & Co outlined a huge c. 400 ton 2-6-6-2 + 2-6-6-2 Mallet/Garratt with about 200,000lb starting tractive effort which would have put even the contemporary American giants in the shade. It was never called for.

The typical Garratt was a sub-standard gauge 4-8-2 + 2-8-4 in Africa, where the biggest user ultimately was the South African Railways. Their largest variant was the 'GL' seen here running bunker first in 1968.
P Ransome Wallis Collection, NRM (PRW 9866)

Garratts were also built for the standard (4ft 8½in) and even 5ft 6in gauges. Particularly notable was the standard gauge 4-8-4 + 4-8-4 for New South wales introduced in 1952. No 6009 is seen at work in 1970 as the steam era in Australia was drawing to a close. *P Ransome Wallis Collection, NRM (PRW 10157)*

Relatively few Mallets were built by British manufacturers, all of them in Glasgow by either NBL or Beardmore's. Here an NBL 1910-built 0-6-6-0 compound of the 5ft 6in gauge Sierra Minera Railway in Spain was recorded in action in 1961.

M D England Collection, NRM

Fireless steam locomotives were extensively employed in German speaking countries. The great majority of the relatively few British examples were built by Andrew Barclay, Sons & Co of Kilmarnock. This late 1956-built example for the Imperial Paper Mills of Gravesend is now preserved in the National Railway Museum at York.

A Listowel & Ballybunion Railway monorail 0-3-0 built by the Hunslet Engine Company in 1887 at work. This unique railway was virtually destroyed in the early 1920s during the Irish Civil War.
NRM/LPC 89902

Each of the four British major locomotive building centres attempted to improve on the very low thermal efficiency of the steam locomotive by breaking the mould.

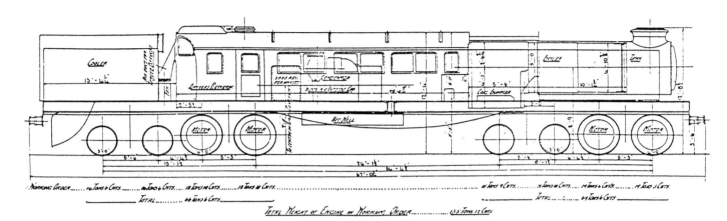

NORTH BRITISH LOCOMOTIVE CO. LTD.
110 FLEMINGTON ST. SPRINGBURN,
GLASGOW.

The experimental steam turbine electric locomotive built by the North British Locomotive Company in 1910. It proved to be a failure.

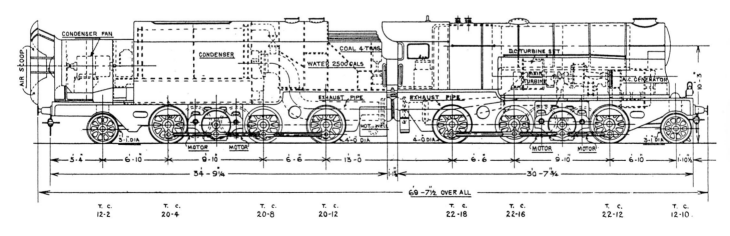

The enormous Ramsay Turbo-Electric condensing locomotive built by Armstrong Whitworth & Co in 1922. Its very high axleload of almost 23 tons greatly restricted the field of its potential operations.

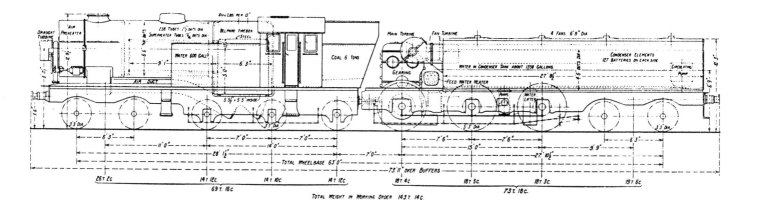

The Ljungstrom steam turbine mechanical condensing locomotive built by Beyer, Peacock &
Co in 1926. It underwent trials on the LMS after which it languished at the builder's works,
even surviving the World War 2 scrap metal drives before being broken up in 1953.

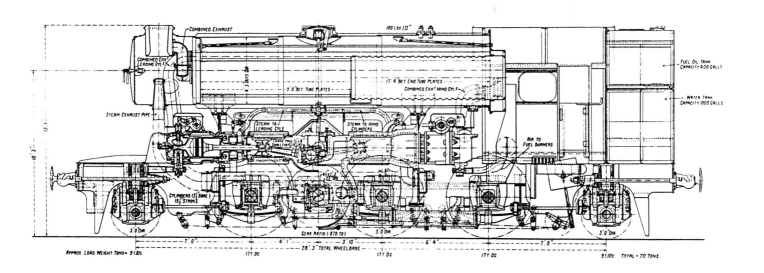

The Kitson Still steam/internal combustion 2-6-2 built by Kitson & Co in 1926. It underwent reasonably successful trials on the LNER, but was probably a major factor in its
builder's financial collapse.

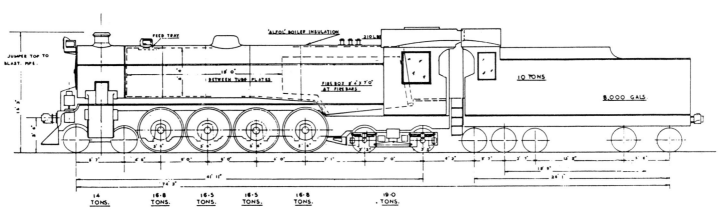

A CASE STUDY — 4-8-4s FOR CHINA

One of the most notable export orders fulfilled by the British locomotive industry was for 24 standard gauge 4-8-4s for China, built by the Vulcan Foundry during 1935-36. These were designed from first principles to meet demanding local requirements, and are worthy of close study as a textbook case of the industry in action, not least reflecting its problems, and the sheer logistics of getting the engines out of the works and shipped to the other side of the world.

1. Historical Background

Known in China as the Yueh-Han line, the Canton - Hankow Railway was first conceived in the 1890s by Cantonese merchants to link the southern port of Canton with Hankow in central China, approximately 600 miles to the north. Its subsequent construction was chequered by warfare over a period of no less than forty years. Soon after construction had been conceded to an American contractor, the American-Spanish War commenced and no survey work was even initiated until a peace treaty had been concluded. There were then severe financial problems and active construction did not begin until 1905. The section north

from Canton had extended 140 miles, whilst the section extending south from Hankow had attained 230 miles when World War 1 broke out in 1914. Construction was then effectively suspended for nearly 20 years because during the 1920s a chaotic situation existed in China which amounted to civil war. By 1929 there was a determination to complete the line, financially aided by the British Boxer Indemnity Fund. The remaining 281 mile section lay through very mountainous terrain, involving ruling gradients of 1 in 80, numerous tunnels, and sharp curvature. Bridges were to be built to a heavier specification than the existing pre-1914 built structures at each end of the line. Under great difficulties this section was largely built between 1933 and 1936, being formally opened in August 1936.

It is sad to relate that scarcely had it begun full operation throughout than the line and its infrastructure were virtually destroyed. The Japanese attacked Canton in October 1937 and thereafter repeatedly bombed the railway, which was also deliberately sabotaged by the Chinese themselves in order to frustrate enemy incursions into the interior. Reconstruction began in December 1945 and remarkably the line was restored to limited operation as early as 1 July 1946.

It was with the completion of the Canton - Hankow Railway in sight that new locomotives were designed and ordered to operate over it. As these were to be financed by the British Boxer Indemnity Fund these would be built by British manufacturers, although distinctly American in concept not least as regards their bar frames and their wheel arrangement.

Roderick Morrison's original 4-8-4 proposal made in Shanghai in February 1933.

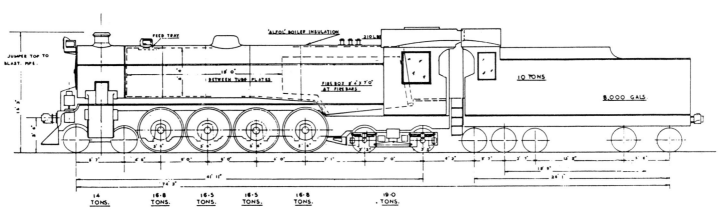

Drawing No	DESCRIPTION	Scale	Drawn No	Order No	By Co	REGISTER		Date
22392	Crosshead & Crosshead Arm	F.3	72				R.P. Bateman	28-6-34
22393	Proposed 4-8-4 Loco.	½" = 1ft		Estimate	Tseh Han	Chinese Purchasing Com.	J.G. Purvor	28-6-34
22394	Proposed 0-8-0 Loco	½" = 1foot		Estimate	Tseh Han	Chinese Purchasing Com.	F. Mc Green	28-6-34
22395	Crosshead ×		—	E.154	Workington		R.P. Bateman	30-6
22396	Intermediate Valve Rod & Valve Spindle	F.S.	844	Estimate	South African	Rly. Harbours.	Twarton	30-6
22397	Alternative Tender for 4-8-4 & 0-8-0 locomotives	5" = 1ft.		E.154	Workington		Cleyland	
22398	Motion Guide & Platform Support	3"=1ft.-F.S.	81				Cleyland	4-7-34
22399	Connecting Rod	F.S.×1ft.-1in	75	E153	Applebt. Iron Co.		R. Fisherman	4-7-34
22400	Hangers, Etc.	FULL SIZE	86	E152	L&S.R.		C.R. Addison	4-7-34
22401	Pipe Clips & Couplings	F.S.	144	E.154	Workington		Cleyland	6-7-34
22402	Coupled Axles & Crank Pins	3"=1ft.-F.S.	41					
22403	Repairs to Smokebox Front	F.S. & H.S.						

The only surviving evidence of Robert Stephenson & Co's submission, June 1934. (The 0-8-0 order, for four engines, went to Armstrong's, who were dismayed at not receiving the 4-8-4 contract.)

NRM

2. Wheel arrangement

?-?-?

Train loading of 600 *tonnes* determined that a starting tractive effort of around 33,000lb was required. Adhesive weight should be around four times this to prevent serious slipping, ie c.60 *tonnes*. This could not be achieved with only three coupled axles.

?-8-?

With regard to the low quality fuel (calorific value 10,800 BThU/lb, ash content 30 per cent) and calculated steam demand (36,000lb/hr) a firegrate area of about 70ft² was estimated, together with a capacious ashpan able to accommodate about 1 ton of ash per hour. This demanded a 4-wheeled trailing truck and mechanical stoker.

?-8-4

The engines would be working on a single track line with passing loops. In order to recover a high final steam temperature (above 800°F) as quickly as possible after stops, an American 'E'-type superheater was considered preferable to a European 'A' type. The penalty was a heavier header in the smokebox, which precluded only a leading pony truck and therefore required a 4-wheeled bogie.

4-8-4

The 4-8-4 wheel arrangement had only recently (1926) made its *début* in the United States, and had just appeared on the 3ft 6in gauge in New Zealand. In many ways it was an *élite* wheel arrangement, wherever it was ultimately found.

3. The Designers

Two Scottish-born locomotive engineers were closely involved in the specification and design of the new 4-8-4s, Kenneth Cantlie and Roderick Morrison. Cantlie had been a premium apprentice of C J Bowen Cooke on the LNWR at Crewe immediately after World War 1. His father, an eminent doctor, had had close links with China around the turn of the century and it was appropriate that the son was appointed as Technical Adviser to the Chinese Ministry of Railways in 1929. Slightly younger than Cantlie, Morrison had served his time on the GWR at Swindon

before going out to China as a technical representative of the Vulcan Foundry in 1931. He produced a scheme for a rather conventional 4-8-4 in February 1933, which was later superseded by Cantlie's rather more advanced 4-8-4 design for which the specification was also prepared in Shanghai, to metric dimensions, in June 1933.

4. Specification

The specification stipulated that 'the locomotives are to present as neat an appearance as possible'. It also indicated that 'the builder is to design the locomotive and tender, incorporating the details as herewith stipulated, as far as practicable. Alterations to the principal dimensions and weights and important details are permitted only with the approval of the Ministry of Railways'.

Certain dimensions were laid down, but others were left to the contractor to determine and hold to:-

Driving wheel diameter 1760mm (5ft 9in)
Adhesive weight . . . . 64 *tonnes* minimum
Engine weight . . . . Not given
Boiler pressure 15.5kg/cm² (220.5lb/in²)
Piston valve diameter 350mm
Cylinder dimensions . . . . Not given
Grate area . . . . 6.2m² (approx) (67ft²)
Boiler diameter . . . . Not given
Tube length 5800mm (19ft)
Combustion chamber length . . . . . 1400mm (approx) (4½ft)

E-type superheater to be accommodated in 120 89mm diameter flues.

Each engine to be fitted with a mechanical stoker, equivalent in design to The Standard Stoker Company Type BK or BK-1.

Tender to have capacity for about 10 *tonnes* of coal and 25m³ (5500 gallons) of water and be on two 4-wheeled trucks.

5. Placing the Order

On the arrival of the first 4-8-4s in Shanghai in March 1936, Roderick Morrison publicly stated:

"Dimensions were deleted from the drawings prior to their being sent out with the calls for tenders. No firm offered exactly what was required but the Vulcan Foundry came nearest to doing so, and its tendered dimensions needed only very slight alterations to fit in with the Ministry's requirements."

45 years later he confessed that '*the final outcome of the contract*

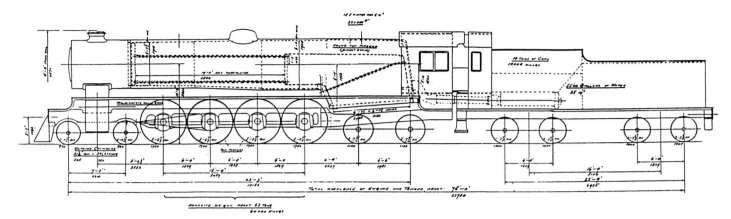

Beyer, Peacock & Co's proposal made on the same day (28 June 1934) as the R. Stephenson & Co. proposal.

---

was a very sad one and reflected very badly on the wisdom of the makers and the locomotive industry'. This somewhat enigmatic statement presumably related to the vexed question of weight, as it was on this basis that Vulcan primarily secured the order. Unfortunately no details of comparative costs survive.

Five leading British locomotive builders submitted tenders, ie

Vulcan Foundry	109 tons (without tender)
Beyer, Peacock & Co	120 tons " "
North British Locomotive Co	124 tons " "
Armstrong Whitworth & Co	135 tons " "
Robert Stephenson & Co	Not known " "

Of these submissions, only that from Beyer, Peacock & Co is known still to exist. Dated 28 June 1934 (as was the corresponding entry in R Stephenson & Co's drawing register) this was endorsed *'To be as light as poss(ible)'*. The range in weights was remarkable, Cantlie himself had estimated 117 tons. It then transpired that in order to get the weight down Vulcan had proposed to use a boiler whose diameter was unacceptably small (c.1850mm) to the Ministry of Railways. As a result this was subsequently enlarged to the diameter Cantlie had anticipated (2000mm), and the actual weight subsequently closely accorded with his estimate.

The original axleload of 16 *tonnes*, to which the Beyer, Peacock scheme would have conformed, was based on the outdated American Cooper method which assumed two short wheelbase 2-8-0 locomotives coupled together and having heavy well-balanced reciprocating parts running at (wheel) diameter speed, ie 56 mph. In fact, double heading would be prohibited and a 4-8-4 locomotive with well spaced 5ft 9in coupled wheels and hollow axles at 50 mph would have a far less dynamic impact on the bridges. On this basis, Cantlie believed even 124 tons engine weight, and an axleload of 17.5 *tonnes* would have been in order.

Vulcan were in the clear but it must have smacked of sharp practice as far as the other builders were concerned.

Vulcan received the order for sixteen engines at a total cost of £92,915 in November 1934, and before even the first was completed eight more were ordered in August 1935, at £87,461. In addition spares to total value £21,744 were ordered, which included seven sets of coupling rods and three pairs of cylinders. The high unit cost of the second batch of engines, compared to the first, which had included 6 engines with tender boosters, will be noted. The tenders were also larger than originally envisaged, running on two 6-wheeled trucks.

6. Tenders

No fewer than 12 alternative tender schemes were prepared at Vulcan for the 4-8-4s. As the first 6 engines were to be fitted with boosters on the leading truck of their tenders, weight had to be saved on these to compensate for the extra weight incurred.

	Variants	Adopted
Wheel configuration:	4-4 or 6-6	6-6
Coal capacity:	7.25...12.0 tonnes	12.0 tonnes
Water capacity:	22.....30m³	30m³ (non-booster)
		27m³ (booster)
Tank construction:	rivetted or welded	welded
Estimated weight (full)	54.5.....79.7 tonnes	78.5 tonnes

7. Shipment

The new 4-8-4s were the longest, but not the heaviest rigid frame steam locomotives so far exported from Britain. The latter were ten 5ft 3in gauge 4-8-2 (later altered to 4-8-4) engines weighing 135 tons (full) for South Australia in 1926 by Armstrong Whitworth & Co. These were shipped dismantled, but with boilers fully clad, painted and with chimneys and cabs attached. Curiously around this time AW had also been building the first Belships for the Norwegian Christen Smith line. These were specifically designed to convey large complete locomotives, and were equipped with deck cranes in order to load and unload the cargo at ports which lacked the necessary dockside craneage.

For despatch from the builders to Birkenhead Docks, the engines were sent as fully-wheeled frames with valve gear set up, fully clad boilers and separate cabs. These are seen on the quayside on 6 November 1935, before re-assembly there prior to loading.

NRM/DY 20530

The first batch of 4-8-4s to be completed (Nos 607 - 612) had to be dismantled after works tests and despatched by rail to Birkenhead. There they were reassembled on the dockside, prior to being loaded on board the *SS Belpamela* in December 1935 for shipment to Shanghai. They were unloaded at the Chinese port in early March 1936.

The shipping details of the four distinct consignments were each different. It is understood that the second batch, Nos 617 - 624, left the Vulcan Works complete and were conveyed by road to the docks, but it is not now known where they were unloaded in China. The earlier three locations reflected the fact that the lengthy Canton - Hankow Railway was still not complete, Tsingtao was particularly remote from it.

Nos.	Condition	Unloaded at
601 - 606 (TB)	complete	Tsingtao
607 - 612	complete	Shanghai
613 - 616	'knocked down'	Canton
617 - 624	complete	not known
TB = tender booster		

8. Operational History

Nos 607 - 612 arrived first in China and were immediately lent to the easily graded Shanghai - Nanking Railway for evaluation. Soon after the Canton - Hankow Railway commenced full operation Japanese forces attacked large areas of China, occupying both Canton and Hankow by late 1938. One 4-8-4 pitched into a river early on in the hostilities and was never recovered, and the remainder eventually fell into the hands of Japanese occupying forces, which made several modifications, including grease lubrication.

By the time World War 2 ended, only sixteen 4-8-4s remained operational and seven were described as being in 'scrap condition'. It was no doubt to repair these that the Canton - Hankow Railway ordered unspecified locomotive spares from Vulcan Foundry in early 1947 to the value of £67,000. After the Communist takeover in China in 1949 little was heard of the 4-8-4s for many years, although Kenneth Cantlie retained his contacts. In 1957 he claimed that an updated version with increased axle-load was to be built, but in fact only limited numbers of 4-6-2s were built for passenger duties until 1966. A 2-10-4 freight equivalent of his 4-8-4 which he had originally proposed in tandem never materialised, and from 1956 large numbers of Russian-designed 2-10-2s were built instead in China itself until 1988.

When US President Nixon made his historic visit to China in 1972, newsreel film revealed his train to be hauled by a Vulcan 4-8-4. Designated KF (Confederation) by the Chinese, the class was seemingly taken out of service from about 1974, but not immediately scrapped.

Unfortunately no photographs appear to exist showing the re-assembly process at Birkenhead, but here is No 611 soon to be swung aboard the SS *Belpamela* alongside.

No 607

In early 1981 a 4-8-4 returned from China deck cargo from Shanghai to Tilbury. It was conveyed thence by road to York for cosmetic restoration by the National Railway Museum as an example of a major British-built steam locomotive export. The engine has been on display since 1983, and was visited by Kenneth Cantlie before his death in 1986. It is surprisingly little altered from its original condition, even retaining the original handsome chimney. The cylinders are Chinese replacements which carry the cast date 12-1964, and it is unclear whether the boiler is a Vulcan-built original as no specific documentation accompanied the engine. Indeed the engine carries no plates or other identification other than a tiny painted digit '7' on the boiler pressure gauge, from which it is presumed to be No 607 (the tender is ex-No 615).

TABLE 16 — Actual Weights of Chinese 4-8-4 Locmotives (Kg) (in full working order)

Engine No.	No 614 (Non-booster)		No 605 (Tender booster)	
Engine	Empty	Full*	Empty	Full*
Leading bogie	20,485	23,548	20,693	23,523
No 1 coupled axle	16,473	17,014	16,494	17,027
No 2 coupled axle	16,393	17,078	16,367	17,154
No 3 coupled axle	16,268	16,951	16,265	17,039
No 4 coupled axle	15,655	16,862	15,771	17,001
Trailing Truck	22,051	25,172	22,178	25,286
Total	107,325	118,625	107,768	117,030
Tender				
Leading bogie	21,404	39,015	24,072	39,648
Trailing bogie	15,708	39,230	16,439	39,014
Total	37,112	78,245	40,511	78,662
Grand total	144,437	194,870	148,279	195,692
Coal capacity		12,000		12,000
Water capacity		30.0m³		27.0m³
Coal		406		406
Sand		103		103
Men		103		103

*Water equivalent to half glass   1000Kg = 2204.6lb = 0.984 tons

About three months later No 610 is unloaded at Shanghai. The vessel involved, the 1927-built (by Armstrong Whitworth) *Belpamela* also conveyed the LMS 4-6-2 No 6229 (masquerading as No 6220 *Coronation*) from Southampton to Baltimore in late 1939. No 6229 *Duchess of Hamilton* is also preserved in the National Collection at York, but sad to relate the *Belpamela* was lost with all hands in a ferocious gale in mid-Atlantic in April 1947 while conveying 16 new 141R 2-8-2s from US builders to France.

NRM 531/83

The first North Eastern Railway 4-6-2 No 2400, designed and built at Darlington Works within the space of eight months, March - November 1922. The photograph is also a superb example of the official works photographer's art. *NRM/DAR 806*

LOCOMOTIVE BUILDING FEATS AND FAULTS

Under ordinary circumstances something like nine to eighteen months would elapse between the ordering and delivery of a batch of steam locomotives. The interval would depend on the delivery of basic materials, eg steel and copper plate, and the workload. If the design was a new one, the design process could occupy several months, although active fabrication would commence well before the final drawings were completed. A new design could also require the preparation of associated patterns and gauges, (necessary anyway in the case of a contract builder). To make a cylinder pattern alone could occupy three months.

Although basically a simple machine, the construction of a steam locomotive required a lot of careful organisation. In 1934 the LMSR revealed some interesting statistics concerning its latest 2-6-4 passenger tank engines. Each would be made up of almost 27,000 distinct components, including 1,475 split pins, most 27,000 distinct components, including 1,475 split pins,

3,350 nuts, 3,500 bolts and set screws, and almost 12,000 rivets! Although not indicated construction was furthermore prescribed by nearly 400 drawings, many newly prepared but some actually dating back as much as 60 years. At the time such engines were being turned out at the rate of two per week from Derby Works.

From time to time, for a variety of reasons, locomotives were required with considerable urgency and were produced with remarkable speed. An early notable example concerned the unique and now preserved Caledonian Railway 4-2-2 No 123. This was ordered from Neilson & Co on 23 January 1886 for delivery to the Edinburgh International Exhibition by 1 April *without fail*. This had to be virtually designed from scratch and yet the engine was indeed delivered within the specified 66 days.

In connection with another exhibition, at Nanking, China in

The unique Caledonian Railway 4-2-2 No 123, which was designed and built in the space of two months in early 1886. (A youthful author stands on the footplate when the engine was on exhibition at Nottingham in November 1953). /GHF Atkins

E 600 360 23/1/86

The Caledonian Railway Co.

4·8½ Gauge.

1 Bogie Express Passenger Engine & Tender to drawings & specification our offer of 22nd inst. and their acceptance of date.

4·2·2+6 Type.   Ins. Cyles. 18×26.   Driving Wheels 7·0 dia.

To be exhibited at the Edinburgh International Exhibition where it must be delivered by 1st April 1886 without fail.

No. 123   Mr Drummond, left of

N° 3553

The entry in Neilson & Co's order book recording the order from the Caledonian Railway for 4-2-2 No 123 in January 1886. /NRM

1910, or rather the traffic this would generate four 4-2-2s were ordered by the Shanghai-Nanking Railway from Kerr, Stuart & Co on 12 April 1910, to be constructed within 45 days. This was not quite achieved, owing to unforeseen circumstances, but the first engine was tested on 8 June, and all were delivered on time.

The all time British record was held by the Hunslet Engine Co of Leeds which received an order from the Benguela Railway on 15 April 1905 for an 0-6-0T and completed it within sixteen working days. It was an amalgamation of two existing designs which nevertheless still required 40 new drawings. The steel plates were delivered on 20 April, the cylinder castings two days later, the boiler was tested on 30 April, and the engine painted on 5 May. Four days later it was dismantled and packed for shipment to West Africa.

Just one year earlier, on 18 March 1904, the Great Central Railway placed a repeat order for five 4-4-2s with Beyer, Peacock & Co. The first engine was tested on 28 June and then spent nearly two weeks in the paint shop before being handed over to the GCR at its Gorton Works, just across the tracks, on 9 July. All five engines had been delivered before the end of that month.

In Glasgow in late 1910 the North British Locomotive Company responded to an urgent enquiry from the French State

3ft gauge Londonderry & Lough Swilly 4-8-4T No 5 at Pennyburn after its final overhaul and repaint in 1950. This was a truly remarkable design for the narrow gauge.

P Ransome Wallis Collection, NRM (PRW 7270)

Railway for 50 general purpose engines. To save time the Highland Railway 'Castle' class 4-6-0 was selected, and a contract signed on 7 January 1911 to deliver the engines 'complete and on rails' in France by 30 June under 'heavy penalty'. Construction was divided 30/20 between two of NBL's three works and all were despatched to France between 15 April and 7 June, a remarkable feat assisted by the design being 'off the peg'.

Railway works could rise to the occasion when required also. On 30 March 1922 Darlington Works received an order for two three-cylinder express passenger 4-6-2s. The first, NER No 2400, was designed and built by early November. This feat was overtaken by Doncaster Works in 1935, when the first four streamlined Gresley Class A4 4-6-2s were ordered in early March. The cylinder drawings were approved on 17 April and the cylinders cast on 6 - 7 June. The first engine, No 2509 *Silver Link*, was completed and first steamed on 7 September, and a locomotive legend was born.

A little known achievement at Crewe Works, LNWR, concerned the construction of the first Webb four-cylinder compound 4-6-0 No 1400. A direct development of the established Class B 0-8-0 heavy goods engines, the first entry in the drawing register, for the frames was dated 23 January 1903, and the first engine authorised seven days later was photographed complete

on 7 March. In view of its affinity with the 0-8-0s, the boiler and cylinders were probably already to hand, and the coupled wheel centres were allegedly second hand, salvaged from withdrawn 0-6-0s. F W Webb's impending retirement might have been the incentive to get the initial engine, which was later followed by 29 others, built so quickly.

The above achievements perhaps did not quite compare with the Baldwin Locomotive Works during World War 1, when it produced a standard gauge 2-8-2 to US Government order within 20 days in 1918, and one year earlier outshopped 2-8-0s for the US Army at the rate of 150 *per month*, or more units than most British builders ever produced in a single year!

Construction is a different matter from assembly, which would also normally occupy several weeks. However, in February 1878 Crewe Works assembled an 0-6-0 coal engine in 25½ working hours (breakfast Monday to mid-day Wednesday), while in December 1891 the Stratford Works of the Great Eastern Railway put together and had in steam another 0-6-0 (GER No 930) in only 10 working hours. Both operations were recorded photographically.

It is probable that most private locomotive builders, and major railway works had a 'skeleton in the cupboard' perpetrated at some time as regards a locomotive which was not entirely what it seemed. This often involved a deception concerning actual and alleged weight. Railway works found it easier to 'cover up' as they were not subject to external inspection procedures. Thus the first and last LMS 4-6-2s weighed several tons more than indicated on the official diagrams, as did the initial Southern Railway 'Pacific' *Channel Packet*. Also locomotives tended to accrue in weight with advancing age as a result of modifications, sometimes to improve performance, but often simply to reinforce main frames etc.

				Diagram Wt (tons)	Actual Wt (tons)
LMS	4-6-2	No 6200	(1933)	104.5	111.9
LMS	4-6-2	No 6257	(1948)	108.5	112.5
SR	4-6-2	No 21C1	(1941)	92.5	99.9
GWR 'King'	4-6-0		(1950s)	89.0	95.9

With private builders it likewise generally amounted to poor estimation. In 1912 Hudswell Clarke & Co supplied two remarkable 3ft gauge 4-8-4Ts to the Londonderry & Lough Swilly Railway which were not supposed to weigh more than 51 tons, but which on completion were found to weigh 58¾ tons. This fact the builder kept to itself for several years in the knowledge that the Irish line had no means of establishing the true amount.

In 1915 Hawthorn Leslie & Co built six large 4-6-0s for the Highland Railway which turned out some 5 - 6 tons heavier than *originally* had been anticipated and which were therefore rejected. The builder was actually in the clear, for the original miscalculation had been made two years earlier by the North British Locomotive Company, which had produced the initial outline scheme and which had simply overlooked the weight of water in the boiler! Hawthorn Leslie itself perpetrated a similar error about five years later when tendering for twelve three-cylinder 2-6-2Ts for South America. The weight of water in the side tanks was completely forgotten and the first engine assembled and weighed, in working order, allegedly causing the chief draughtsman to threaten to commit suicide. This engine, and the eleven remaining units were then drastically revamped as 2-6-4Ts with short side tanks.

Hawthorn's were left with twelve redundant pony trucks on its hands, but waited in vain for a repeat order. Such in the event went to the Vulcan Foundry and North British Locomotive Company, for what was considered to be a superior design than the 2-6-2T which had originally been envisaged.

Occasionally the larger builders 'got it wrong' and on a heroic scale, most notably Beyer, Peacock & Co. with three *six*-cylinder 4-6-2 + 2-6-4 Garratts for New Zealand. Delivered in 1929 these were conspicuously absent from BP's lavish 1947 Garratt catalogue, not least because the engines had been dismantled after only seven years (and converted to six indifferent 4-6-2 tender engines). It seems likely that the builder's own more conservative proposals would have been more successful, but the NZGR CME, G S Lynde, (an ex-Great Central man) had overreached himself and specified a too powerful and too complicated locomotive which traffic conditions did not justify. In other respects the Beyer Garratt in general was the enduring success story of 20th century British locomotive engineering whose maximum possible potential was never realised.

The prototype Southern Railway 4-6-2 No.21C1 *Channel Packet* 'carefully' designed to incorporate weight-saving measures such as welding to achieve an axleload of 21 tons, in practice the engine weighed more than 7 tons over the estimate. Stringent measures were applied to the third engine onwards, including elimination of the three gratuitously heavy numberplates carried by the engine, and 'Southern' plates on the tender. The engine is shown as brand new in March 1941. *NRM 395/8/66*

LOCOMOTIVE BUILDING CENTRES

Commercial steam locomotive building in Great Britain became concentrated primarily in four areas, North East England, North West England, Glasgow and Leeds. The industry originated in Newcastle-upon-Tyne in the 1820s, but by the 1840s the North East had been overtaken by the North West. In due course, by the late 1880s, Glasgow had become pre-eminent. Each of these areas also contained railway works whose output was also significant. Leeds, however, was exceptional, for sixty years (1866-1926) it contained five commercial builders in very close proximity with each other, but there were never any *railway* works in that city.

Railway works tended to be located at strategic points on the railways which they served, with little regard to the logistics of supply of raw materials. Private locomotive builders, on the other hand, tended to be well placed for coal and iron supplies, hence their preponderance in the North of England and industrial Scotland. Having said this, Sheffield accommodated only a single small locomotive builder. The greater significance of Leeds and Manchester can probably be attributed, at least in part to the prior establishment in these cities of the textile industry, the only precedent for precision engineering. Some early locomotive building enterprises actually pre-dated the railway era and were initially involved with the textile industry, whose magnitude has been largely forgotten in more recent times.

The proliferation of locomotive building in Manchester and Glasgow was no coincidence. In each city a senior (German) partner with the leading manufacturer of the time broke away to found his own enterprise. In Leeds, complex personal links existed between the different builders, and there is little doubt that a strong measure of informal 'freemasonry' existed between the different builders even before the establishment of the Locomotive Manufacturers Association in 1875.

1. North East England

The commercial manufacture of steam locomotives commenced in Newcastle-upon-Tyne in 1825 with the 0-4-0 *Locomotion* for the Stockton & Darlington Railway, and continued on the same site for 133 years. Robert Stephenson & Co set up in business in Forth Street, below where Newcastle Central station would be built twenty years later, next door to R & W Hawthorn & Co, with whom it would amalgamate over a century later.

In 1829 Stephenson's built the 0-2-2 *Rocket*, the world's first truly conventional steam locomotive with multitubular boiler, and exhaust steam to create a self regulating draught on the fire. The following year appeared the almost equally significant 2-2-0 *Planet* with inside cylinders, for the Liverpool & Manchester Railway. The firm and its products literally became world famous, and indeed these would soon be found in many parts of the world. The 'Patentee' 2-2-2 (1833) was a logical development of *Planet*, and another speciality was the 'long boiler' engine most commonly an 0-6-0. Stephenson's also early on showed a predilection for four-wheel leading trucks, building a diminutive 4-2-0 for the Schenectady & Saratoga Railroad (USA) as early as 1833, and was building 4-4-0s by 1855, including some inside-cylinder broad gauge engines (the 'Waverley' class) for the GWR.

OPPOSITE

An aerial photograph of the Hunslet district in south Leeds. Taken in the late 1940s, by this time at least six distinct enterprises in the small area in view had produced more than 10,000 steam locomotives during the course of a century. Many of these were relatively small industrial and narrow gauge engines, but most of the 4,000 produced by the then defunct Kitson & Co in the Airedale Foundry, which dominates the top of the photograph, were of the main line variety, including many for export. Jack Lane, the postal address of almost all the other builders, runs across the centre.

TABLE 18 — The Location of the Private British Steam Locomotive Building Industry 1875-1950

	1875	1900	1925	1950
Glasgow	Neilson (1836) Dübs (1864)	Neilson,Reid (1897) Dübs Sharp Stewart (from 1888)	North British Locomotive (1903) { W Beardmore (1920-31)	North British Locomotive (1962†)
Kilmarnock	A Barclay (1840)	A Barclay	A Barclay	A Barclay
Newcastle	R Stephenson (1823) R & W Hawthorn (1817)	R Stephenson R & W Hawthorn Leslie (1884)	(see Darlington) R & W Hawthorn Leslie Armstrong Whitworth (1919-37)	R Stephenson & Hawthorns (1937) (1960†)
Darlington	—	—	R Stephenson (from 1902)	R Stephenson & Hawthorns (1937) (1964†)
Leeds	Kitson (1835) Manning Wardle (1858) Hudswell Clarke (1860) Hunslet (1864) J Fowler (1850)	Kitson Manning Wardle Hudswell Clarke Hunslet Engine J Fowler	Kitson (1938†) Manning Wardle (1926†) Hudswell Clarke Hunslet Engine J Fowler (1964†)	— — Hudswell Clarke (1970†) Hunslet Engine (1996†)
Sheffield	Yorkshire Engine (1865)	Yorkshire Engine	Yorkshire Engine	Yorkshire Engine (1965†)
Manchester (inc Salford)	Nasmyth Wilson (1836) Sharp Stewart (1828) Beyer, Peacock (1854)	Nasmyth Wilson (see Glasgow) Beyer, Peacock	Nasmyth Wilson (1939†) — Beyer, Peacock	— Beyer, Peacock (1966†)
Newton-le-Willows	Vulcan Foundry (1830)	Vulcan Foundry	Vulcan Foundry	Vulcan Foundry (1970†)
Stoke	—	Kerr Stuart (1893)	Kerr Stuart (1930†)	—
Stafford	W G Bagnall (1875)	W G Bagnall	W G Bagnall	W G Bagnall (1962†)
Bristol	Avonside Engine (1866) Fox Walker (1864)	Avonside Engine Peckett (1882)	Avonside (1934†) Peckett	— Peckett (c.1962†)

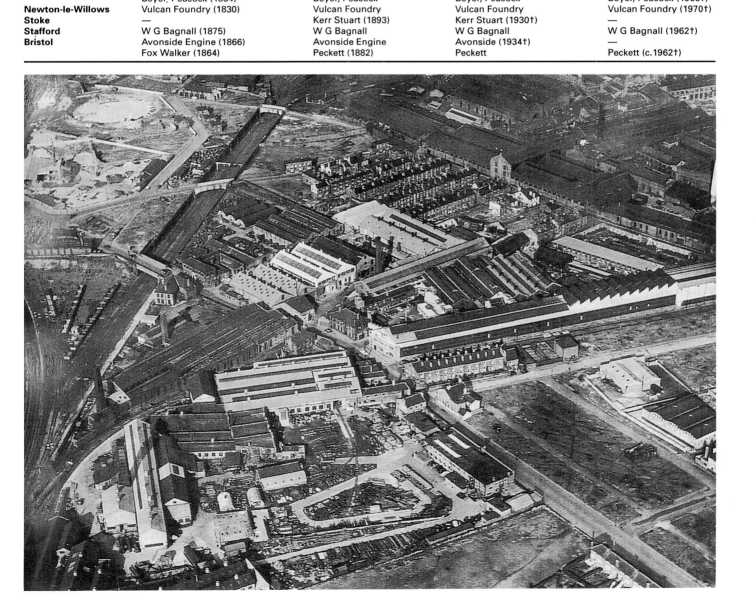

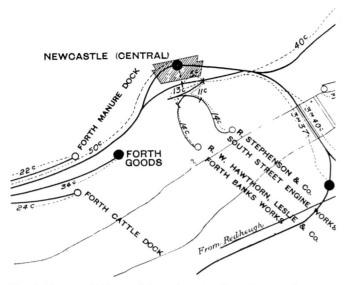

North Eastern Railway siding plan showing the complex access arrangement to both Robert Stephenson & Co and R & W Hawthorn Leslie & Co in Newcastle-upon-Tyne pre-1900. New standard gauge locomotives leaving the respective works had to undergo reversals and climb inclines as steep as 1 in 13 to gain access to the NER above. The Gateshead (NER) works and Black Hawthorn & Co. were just across the river.

Towards the end of the 19th century the Company was reorganised twice and the decision was taken to remove to a greenfield site at Darlington, where production commenced in 1902. Ironically, maximum annual production there, at 59 in 1914, although the average size of the locomotives would have been larger, did not even approach the 96 achieved at Newcastle in 1868. The largest engines built in Darlington would have been the poppet valve Class 15E 4-8-2s for the South Africa Railways in 1935.

R & W Hawthorn commenced locomotive production in 1831 and initially, like many of its contemporaries, made some-thing of a speciality of building 2-2-2s. For quite a number of years after about 1860, its contribution to the domestic market was small, other than building some 4-4-0s and 0-6-0s for the North Eastern Railway in 1884, specialising more in industrial locomotives and exports overseas. Following the removal of Stephenson's in 1901 it eventually expanded and about 1913 began to take on orders for quite large locomotives, 0-6-4Ts for the Barry Railway (1914), large superheater 4-6-0s for the Highland (1915) and 2-8-2s for China (1921). In 1850 Hawthorn's had set up a subsidiary in Leith, near Edinburgh to assemble locomotives for Scottish railways from parts sent by sea from Newcastle. This reflected the then fragmented nature of the British railway system and the problems of delivery. Production ceased there in 1886.

In 1937, R & W Hawthorn Leslie & Co (as it had become in 1884) amalgamated with Robert Stephenson & Co to form Robert Stephenson & Hawthorns Ltd. Thereafter the Newcastle works tended to concentrate on industrial locomotives and Darlington the larger main line contracts. The last steam locomotive to be built at Forth Banks, an 0-6-0ST, was outshopped in October 1958, 133 years after *Locomotion*.

The general level of locomotive building in the North East did not really compare with that in Glasgow or Manchester, except in the early 1920s when Armstrong Whitworth & Co provided a considerable boost giving an unusually late overall peak in 1921. In fact, in the course of barely 18 years Armstrong's built approximately the same number of steam locomotives as did Nasmyth, Wilson & Co in a century.

Another Tyneside locomotive builder, all too easily forgotten, was Black Hawthorn & Co (yet another Hawthorn!) of Gateshead, which together with its shortlived successor, Chapman & Furneaux, produced something like 800 mainly industrial locomotives in Gateshead between 1866 and 1902.

Although Stephenson's exported all over the world, a significant customer was Turkey, several of whose railway companies were originally British owned. In 1907 a small batch of outside-cylinder 0-8-0s of distinctly Great Central appearance, was supplied to the Ottoman Railway, of which one was photographed at Izmir fifty years later. *P Ransome Wallis Collection, NRM (PRW 5869)*

A Sharp Stewart speciality was the inside-cylinder 0-4-0, tank or tender, whose origins could be traced back to Edward Bury via Fairbairn & Co. Furness Railway No 27 was a late example built in 1866, an update of 'Coppernob'. The bell-shaped dome with Salter safety valves later became a standard feature on the Midland Railway locomotives of S W Johnson.   *NRM LPC 14639*

2. North West England

The first locomotives to be built outside the North East were built in Liverpool, where Edward Bury flourished for nearly twenty years producing distinctive 2-2-0 and 0-4-0 locomotives, and latterly 2-2-2s and 2-4-0s with bar frames and hemispherical fireboxes. Having built 400 locomotives the firm folded in 1850, but across the River Mersey the Canada Works of Brassey & Co built about 200 locomotives between 1854 and 1875.

Between Liverpool and Manchester at Newton-le-Willows (through which the new Liverpool & Manchester Railway passed) Charles Tayleur established the Vulcan Foundry in 1830, commencing locomotive production three years later, by which time Stephenson's had a financial interest. Vulcan supplied the first locomotives in India in 1852 and ultimately almost exactly half of its total steam locomotive production was destined for the subcontinent, the final delivery being over a century later in 1955. Vulcan's greatest single achievement, however, was probably the 24 4-8-4s for China described in Chapter 8. A second locomotive builder, Jones, Turner & Evans was founded in Newton-le-Willows in 1837. Re-styled Jones & Potts in 1844 it ceased locomotive production in 1852.

Closer to Manchester two enterprises commenced locomotive building in 1839, Nasmyth Wilson & Co in Patricroft, and William Fairbairn in central Manchester. The latter built about 400 locomotives until 1863, some of which saw service abroad until well into the 20th century. Nasmyth Wilson & Co manufactured a number of products, including James Nasmyth's patent steam hammer. There were several periods during its long history when no locomotives were built at all. Undoubtedly the most remarkable engines ever built at the Bridgewater Foundry were two 5ft 6in gauge 106 ton 2-10-2Ts for the Bombay Port Trust in 1922. A high proportion of the company's output was in fact built for India.

Pre-eminent in Manchester for about fifty years was Sharp Stewart & Co, which as Sharp Roberts had built its first locomotive in 1833. The firm initially had strong involvement with the textile industry. Sharp's subsequent achievements on such a restricted non-rail connected site were remarkable. Eight-coupled tank locomotives were being built as early as 1866, and some 0-8-0 tender engines were built for Russia in 1871. During the later 1870s a semi-'standard' 0-8-0 was designed which would see service as far afield as Spain, and in Scandinavia as far north as the Arctic Circle. After their 1888 removal to Glasgow, Sharp Stewart would build 4-6-0s in remarkably similar mould for the Highland Railway in 1894, - a British first. In 1834 Sharp's had recruited a young Saxon, Charles Beyer (1813-1876) who showed a remarkable aptitude for locomotive design, combining simple elegance with function, which first became apparent in 2-2-2s built in the early 1840s. Beyer's simple yet elegant style was facilitated by the increasing use of steel in locomotive construction and persisted long after his death. The

The Sheffield & Manchester Railway long-boiler 0-6-0 *Sphynx*, built by Sharp's in 1848 was an extrapola-
tion of the classic Sharp 0-4-0 and a remarkably powerful locomotive for its day. Other examples were built
for the Southern Division of the LNWR.

There were strong links between Beyer, Peacock & Co and John Ramsbottom of the LNWR, which was first
expressed in the latter's prolific 'DX' 0-6-0 (943 built). The ultimate descendant of these was the G2 0-8-0
of 1921-22 of which No 134 is pictured brand new. Over seventy years on several features of *Sphynx* are
discernible, ie H-section wheel spokes, and rectangular cab side sheets.   *NRM/W4350*

Mersey Railway 0-6-4T No 1 built by Beyer Peacock & Co in 1885. Although the most powerful British locomotive built to date it was an archaic combination of long boiler with double frames.

highly acclaimed lineaments of S W Johnson's late 19th century locomotives on the Midland Railway, and those of J G Robinson on the Great Central Railway in the early 20th century, can be directly traced back to the influence of Charles Beyer, whose full impact has yet to be evaluated. Designers of German birth or German descent held prominent positions at Peacock's, as the firm was locally known, until as late as 1927.

In 1848 Beyer designed a powerful single-framed long-boiler 0-6-0 for the Sheffield & Manchester Railway, whose Locomotive Superintendent was Richard Peacock (1820-1889). Born in Arkengarthdale, North Yorkshire, as a boy of five Peacock had witnessed the opening of the Stockton & Darlington Railway in September 1825. At the remarkably early age of 18 he was ap-

The nine Mersey 0-6-4Ts must have left something to be desired because when further locomotives were soon required, remarkably advanced (for the 1880s) outside-cylinder 2-6-2Ts were produced. As before, condensing gear and open cabs were provided. These six engines were leased by the builders.

pointed Locomotive Superintendent of the Leeds & Selby Railway. On the S & MR he had carefully planned its locomotive works to be situated at Gorton, in the then still rural east Manchester. In 1853 he resigned his post to set up in business with Beyer to establish a new locomotive building venture, also to be located in Gorton. Beyer, Peacock & Co despatched its first locomotive to the Great Western Railway (a 2-2-2) in July 1855.

An S W Johnson Midland Railway 4-4-0, No 2592, built by Neilson, Reid & Co in 1901.

N Thompson Collection, NRM (JHLA G550)

Export orders rapidly followed, the firm quickly becoming renowned for the high standard of design and the quality of its products. BP was the first British locomotive builder to be specifically founded as such, although a major sideline was the supply of machine tools.

In 1909 the first Beyer Garratt articulated locomotive was built, and such became a major speciality over the next fifty years, although the maximum potential of the type was never realised. The Gorton Foundry closed in 1966, (three years after Gorton Works alongside) but the former erecting shop is the only remaining landmark of either establishment to survive demolition, serving as a municipal vehicle depot.

The Beyer-style as regards sweeping coupled wheel splashers and chimney profiles could be detected in the elegant inside-cylinder 4-4-0s of several railways from the Glasgow & South Western to the South Eastern & Chatham designed around the turn of the century. Also the elegant oiling apertures could be traced back to the 1840s, eg *Sphynx*.

An H S Wainwright South Eastern & Chatham Railway Class D in its prime, No 729, built by Sharp Stewart & Co in 1901. The affinity with the MR 4-4-0 is particularly strong, not least the flush smokebox door.

3. Glasgow

Ultimately one third of all commercially-built steam locomotives in Britain, and almost one fifth of all such locomotives were built in the city of Glasgow.

The dominating enterprise was Neilson & Co, which originated c. 1837 building stationary and marine engines, before building its first locomotives for the Glasgow, Garnkirk & Coatbridge Railway six years later. Within twenty years the original works became inadequate and in the early 1860s the enterprise removed to a site in Springburn between the St Rollox Works of the Caledonian Railway and the Cowlairs Works of the North British Railway. This works was named the Hyde Park Works after the street on which the earlier works had been situated. Involved in the planning was the German, Henry Dübs (1816-1876) who had arrived in England and found successive employment with Sharps in Manchester, as works manager at the Vulcan Foundry, and worked briefly for Beyer, Peacock & Co soon after its foundation.

No sooner had Dübs designed the new Neilson works, than he left to establish a new enterprise of his own at Polmadie, the Glasgow Locomotive Works (which was renamed the Queen's Park Works in 1903). Like Neilson's, Dübs & Co soon got heav-

ily involved in exporting locomotives overseas as well as supplying the domestic market. Henry Dübs himself was credited with the then revolutionary notion of employing women tracers, thereby releasing male draughtsmen for new design work.

Meanwhile Walter Neilson was effectively forced out of the firm he had helped to found, in 1876, but eight years later he returned to establish the Clyde Locomotive Company in Springburn. This only built some thirty locomotives between 1886 and 1888, before it was taken over by Sharp, Stewart & Co on the latter's removal to Glasgow, the premises thereupon becoming known as the Atlas Works after the Manchester plant whose lease had expired thus enforcing its vacation.

In the closing years of the 19th century all three Glasgow builders met a considerable proportion of domestic demand before amalgamating on 1 April 1903 to form the North British Locomotive Company. The theoretical capacity of NBL was approximately equal to that of the remaining (English) builders put together. Strangely, it did not always seem to live up to its giant reputation. Around 1910 the North British *Railway* went to builders in England for 4-4-2s and 4-4-2Ts, and soon afterwards the Highland Railway, a former customer of long standing,

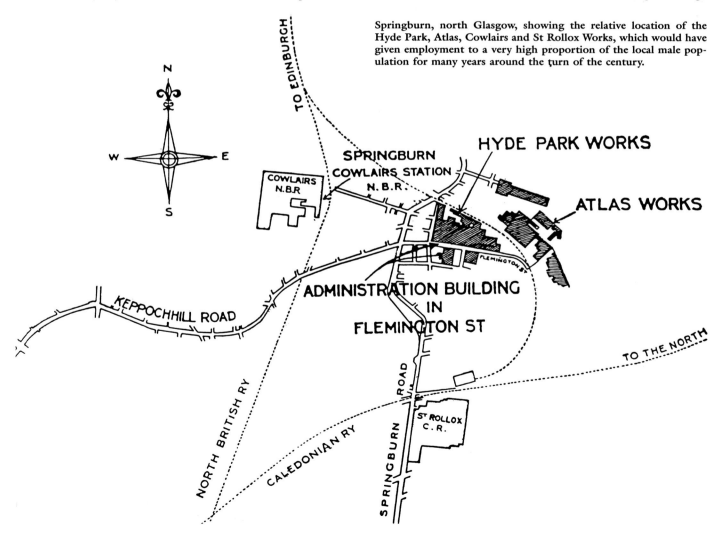

Springburn, north Glasgow, showing the relative location of the Hyde Park, Atlas, Cowlairs and St Rollox Works, which would have given employment to a very high proportion of the local male population for many years around the turn of the century.

Glasgow-built locomotives were exported all over the world, but the largest single customer after World War 2 was the South African Railways.

The ultimate development of the SAR 4-8-2 was the 15F, of which NBL built the final series in 1948. A typical example at Pretoria in 1968. *P Ransome Wallis Collection, NRM (PRW 9778)*

forged a close relationship with R & W Hawthorn Leslie in Newcastle.

NBL opened a lavish new administration block in Flemington Street, Springburn in 1909 (which still survives as a technical college) soon after which the firm never really regained its former glory. Reduced demand after 1920 resulted in the closure of the Atlas Works in 1923, although this was the most recent plant to have been built.

The building of locomotives in railway works in Glasgow also ceased during the 1920s, as a result of the railway amalgamations in 1923. There was considerable anger at Cowlairs in 1949 at the prospect of possible redundancies at a time when NBL was

building 4-6-0s of former LNER design for the newly formed British Railways. By the final decade of steam locomotive building at NBL the latter's output did not always equal the combined production of the Vulcan Foundry and Beyer, Peacock & Co and so it might be said that Glasgow was no longer pre-eminent at the very end. Indeed the last *major* steam order to be taken by North British was a sub-contract from Beyer, Peacock for twenty Garratts for South Africa (which this time were manufactured perfectly legitimately).

The end, when it came, was little short of tragic. NBL's entry into the diesel market ultimately proved disastrous, and Britain's largest locomotive builder's demise mirrored that of the USA's six years earlier. There was a strong irony in that the North British Locomotive Company had originally come into being to meet the perceived threat posed by the Baldwin Locomotive Works. However, at 59,000, it is salutory to consider that Baldwin's total steam locomotive production had almost exactly equalled the *combined* production of the major British locomotive builders over an identical period. But then Baldwin's accounted for one in eleven of all the steam locomotives ever built!

A development of the 15F was the Class 25 4-8-4 built 1953-55. This incorporated cast steel engine beds imported from the USA and roller bearings. A conventional example at Kimberley in 1968.
P Ransome Wallis Collection, NRM (PRW 9820)

OPPOSITE

Fifty 4-8-4s were also built with condensing tenders for operation across the arid Karoo desert. These huge tenders were almost as large as the engines, one of which was pictured leaving De Aar in 1968.   *P Ransome Wallis Collection, NRM (PRW 9809)*

4. Leeds

Steam locomotives, and indeed locomotives in general, were built for longer in the city of Leeds than anywhere else on earth. As elsewhere, the great bulk were built between the 1830s and the 1950s, but the first was built exceptionally early, in 1812, and the last unusually late, in 1971, giving a span of all but 150 years. (Diesel locomotives continued to be built in diminishing numbers for a further 25 years until 1995).

It all began with the Round Foundry, established in 1795, where Fenton Murray & Wood completed two rack locomotives for the Middleton Colliery in Leeds in August 1812, to the designs of John Blenkinsop. Two more quickly followed, but formal locomotive construction for the 'main line' era did not commence until 1831 with two 2-2-0s for the Liverpool & Manchester Railway. Production ended in 1841-42 with seventeen broad gauge 2-2-2s for the GWR, some time before which Richard Peacock had served his time with the firm at the outset of an eminent career in locomotive engineering.

Another trainee at the Round Foundry was Charles Todd, who became a partner in Todd, Kitson & Laird, the short-lived forerunner of Kitson & Co of the Airedale Foundry. He was also a founder of the Railway Foundry, both in Hunslet. Kitson's became the dominant locomotive builder in Leeds for almost a

A rare locomotive survival from the 1830s, the least represented decade from the 1820s to the 1950s in the British locomotive pantheon, the Liverpool & Manchester Railway 0-4-2 *Lion*, built by Todd, Kitson & Laird in 1837 and now preserved. *NRM DM 819*

century. Ironically it had had a prior approach by H W Garratt before the latter impressed Beyer, Peacock & Co with his articulated system. Kitson's made something of a speciality of building Kitson-Meyer locomotives, but only produced about 70 of these, whereas Beyer, Peacock & Co went on to build over one thousand Garratts over a period of 50 years. Kitson's suffered a lingering death. In bad financial shape from 1924 it went into receivership in 1934 but only finally totally expired in 1945. Although its goodwill was purchased by Robert Stephenson & Hawthorns, very few of its primary records have survived.

Meanwhile the Railway Foundry passed through a series of ownerships culminating with E B Wilson in 1846. The latter quickly developed a truly international market which initially rivalled Kitson's, and produced its own highly successful brand of 2-2-2, the 'Jenny Lind'. Sadly, a legal action closed the enterprise in 1850 despite a number of orders still outstanding.

The Railway Foundry premises were then divided to become partially those of Hudswell Clarke & Co, in 1860, and the Hunslet Engine Company in 1864, each of which would build steam locomotives, primarily for industrial purposes, for a century. Even so, Hudswell Clarke never built a locomotive with a superheater, but Hunslet's products were much more diverse. These ranged from the unique twin-boilered 0-3-0 monorail engines for the Listowel & Ballybunnion Railway in Ireland (1887) to two massive superheated 84 ton 0-8-0Ts for China in 1933-34.

Although Edgar Alcock, Hunslet's managing director, foresaw the eventual rise of the diesel locomotive much earlier than most, reputedly by 1920, his firm stuck to steam while developing the diesel. Active measures were taken in the late 1950s and early 1960s to try and avoid contravening the Clean Air Act, 1956 which had virtually sounded the death knell for the industrial steam locomotive in Britain, and the firm also increased its boiler shop facilities in order to meet an anticipated continuing demand from overseas for spares. Two new 0-6-0STs were delivered to the National Coal Board as late as March 1964, and a 750mm gauge 0-4-2ST of 1905 design to Indonesia in 1971.

The firm finally closed down in 1996 after a series of amalgamations in its closing years including with Andrew Barclay in 1972.

Adjoining both Hudswell Clarke and the Hunslet Engine Company was the Boyne Engine Works of Manning Wardle Ltd, which likewise specialised in 0-4-0Ts and 0-6-0Ts. In the early 20th century it actively promoted the patent Marshall and Isaacson valve gears, and a subsidiary even manufactured Isaacson radial aero engines for a period just prior to 1914.

Manning Wardle was the first British locomotive builder active in the early 20th century to pass out of business (in 1926) after which its premises were taken over by the Hunslet Engine Co and its goodwill was sold to Kitson & Co, who subsequently built a few 0-6-0Ts to Manning Wardle designs.

One further locomotive builder was active in the area. John Fowler & Co of the Steam Plough Works. The latter was established in 1850 to manufacture agricultural machinery, but a major collapse in the cotton industry in the 1860s resulted in a diversification into locomotive building in 1866, at a time when there was a high demand. Although initially 'main line' locomotives were produced for the domestic market, increasingly narrow gauge plantation steam locomotives were built, the last in 1935. The manufacture of small diesel locomotives continued until 1964. Interestingly, rail access to the adjoining Airedale Foundry of Kitson & Co passed right through the Steam Plough Works.

A brand new Furness Railway 4-6-4T emerges from the Airedale Foundry on a bleak winter's day in late 1920. These engines were towed dead from Leeds to Barrow prior to commissioning.
NRM 3640/76

The last Hudswell Clarke steam locomotive and 0-4-0ST, delivered to of the National Coal Board in September 1961, seen at work in 1972. By this time active industrial steam locomotives were scarce, a sister engine stands out of use in the background.
T Heavyside

The last standard gauge and penultimate steam locomotive to be built in Britain, a modified Hunslet 'Austerity' 0-6-0ST stands out of use at Cadeby Main Colliery, South Yorkshire, on its 10th anniversary in March1974. This engine is now privately preserved.   / *T. Heavyside*

Peckett locomotives, usually 0-4-0STs
and 0-6-0STs, were highly
standardised but customised as to
detail. A special one-off was this 2ft
gauge 0-6-2ST for the Harrogate Gas
Works Railway.
NRM/IRS (P 23/31)

A myriad of small builders, often
general engineers, also built small
numbers of industrial 0-4-0Ts and
0-6-0Ts. Particularly outstanding were
those built by Guest, Keen &
Nettlefold for its own use which were
virtually the only standard gauge steam
locomotives to be built anywhere in
Wales after 1900. This particularly
massive example was built at Dowlais
in 1907.
R T Russell Collection NRM (RTR 748)

5. Other Centres

Although the most important locomotive building centres were located in the North of England and Glasgow, there were also others.

In **Bristol** the Avonside Engine Company and Peckett & Sons and their antecedents collectively produced approaching four thousand steam locomotives, - a surprisingly high total. Peckett's products were quite distinctive, the 0-4-0 saddle tank was *the basic steam locomotive* yet its styling varied considerably from builder to builder and usually left little doubt as to its origin.

Stoke (on Trent) contained the works of Kerr Stuart & Co and the North Staffordshire Railway. Only established in 1893, by 1914 the former was active in the export business, especially to South America. Some engines thus destined carried carefully styled chimneys resembling those on the NSR, whose architect had been B K Field, late of the South Eastern Railway.

Similarly, **Kilmarnock** contained the works of Andrew Barclay Sons & Co, and of the Glasgow & South Western Railway. Barclay industrials rather lacked the refinement of those of other builders. Barclay's made a particular speciality of building fireless steam accumulator locomotives, producing 114 between 1912 and 1962, out of 161 British examples built in total. Unusually, the firm built a batch of Class 4F superheated 0-6-0s for the LMSR in 1928. Its final steam locomotive, a narrow gauge plantation 0-6-2 tender engine for Indonesia, subcontracted from W G Bagnall & Co, was shipped in 1962. In 1998, in recent years styled Hunslet-Barclay, this enterprise is the only former British steam locomotive builder to remain in existence.

Bagnall's, referred to above, were the major locomotive builders in **Stafford**, where the firm tended to specialise in industrial and narrow gauge locomotives. In 1950 the Castle Engine Works produced the 'ultimate industrial', three powerful outside cylinder 0-6-0STs, with Walschaerts valve gear, piston valves and roller bearing big ends for The Steel Company of Wales.

In its later years the Yorkshire Engine Company in **Sheffield** was associated with a modest output of industrial tank engines, but this had not always been the case. In the 1870s it built double Fairlie articulated tank engines, and in 1907 fifteen large inside-cylinder 0-8-0s for the Hull & Barnsley Railway. In the 1920s narrow gauge 4-8-2s and 4-8-4Ts were built for South America, whilst particularly notable was a prototype three-cylinder 5ft 6in gauge 4-8-0 with trapezoidal grate for Spain (1921). Surprisingly, in 1998 the Meadowhall Works still stand, **not** submerged beneath the huge shopping complex which has also taken its name from that part of Sheffield.

This is not a typical scenario, however, since the early 1960s most British former steam locomotive building plants have been erased from the landscape.

It is interesting to note that about 85 per cent of commercial locomotive construction took place in the four main eras earlier mentioned, and 65 per cent of locomotive construction in railway works occurred in 'railway towns' which did not also contain commercial locomotive builders. Obviously this proportion was heavily weighted by Crewe and Swindon, which had a combined production in excess of 13,000 locomotives. Each of these achieved a maximum annual output of around 150 locomotives, whereas the greatest production by a single *private* works was 236 by Neilsons in 1886. The latter facts, both the modest magnitude and the relatively early date in themselves speak volumes regarding the nature of the British locomotive industry even when it was in its undisputed prime.

TABLE 19 — Estimated Total Production of British Steam Locomotive Building Centres

	Private Builders	Railway Works	Total	Period
Glasgow	23,750	*2,000*	**25,750**	1835-1958
North West England				
Manchester	13,100	*1,500*	14,600	1833-1958
Merseyside	7,300	*40*	7,300	1827-1956
Bolton area	300	*1,800*	2,100	1831-1957
			24,000	
North East England				
Newcastle	7,750	—	7,750	1825-1958
Gateshead	1,200	*1,000*	2,200	1849-1910
Darlington	1,400	*2,250*	3,650	1864-1957
			13,600	
Leeds	11,000	—	**11,000**	1831-1964
				(1812-1971)
Bristol	3,900	*35*	**c.4,000**	1841-1958
London	c150	*2,750*	**2,900**	1843-1924
Kilmarnock	2,100	*400*	**2,500**	1857-1962
Stoke-on-Trent	1,500	*200*	**1,700**	1868-1930
Stafford	c.1,700	—	**1,700**	1876-1957
Sheffield	c.800	—	**800**	1866-1956
'Railway Towns' (Railway Works only)	—	*21,900*	**21,900**	1843-1960

Epilogue

The commercial manufacture of steam locomotives came to an end in no fewer than eight British towns and cities with remarkable conformity between 1956 and 1958 (which was also mirrored by all but one of seven active railway works at this period). A handful of minor orders remained to be undertaken in Kilmarnock and Leeds during the early 1960s.

Just ten years after the end of World War 2 the demand for new steam locomotives, for either domestic service or from overseas, main line or industrial, had dried up. During this period in the United States the diesel-electric locomotive had increased its haulage of the national railway traffic from 10 per cent to 90 per cent, and the trend was beginning to be reflected elsewhere in the world, together with increasing main line electrification.

However, it would be wrong to believe that the British locomotive industry had been totally wrong-footed on this fundamental issue. The diesel locomotive first made its appearances on shunting duties and most of the smaller locomotive builders, especially those in Leeds and Newcastle built their first diesel locomotives during the early 1930s despite and also because of the dire economic situation, ie the promise of greatly reduced operating costs. The family run firm of Peckett's did not finally acknowledge that times were indeed changing until about 1954, about three years after Bagnall's had produced its first diesel locomotive.

Armstrong Whitworth & Co, a newcomer to locomotive building, early recognised the future potential of the diesel locomotive as did Beardmore's. However, in the 1930s, North British in a manner reminiscent of its American counterparts, preferred not to consider diesel traction to be a potential threat to the long established steam locomotive, and did not take on its first main line diesel order until 1947, from the LMS for an 800 HP Bo-Bo of pure American concept. Vulcan had already entered into a licensing agreement for diesel engine manufacture with the Danish enterprise Frichs of Aarhus in 1934, and in 1949 Beyer, Peacock & Co, together with its fellow Mancunian manufacturer Metropolitan Vickers set up a plant to build non-steam locomotives at Bowesfield near Stockton-on-Tees.

Just as British commercial steam locomotive manufacture was rapidly tapering to vanishing point, the British Railways Re-Equipment and Modernisation Plan, published in January 1955 gave a new boost to the private industry. Although originally this plan envisaged a limited number of pilot diesel locomotives which were to be evaluated over a period of three years service up to 1960 prior to large orders being placed, in the event the timescale was hurried forward, initially to the delight of former steam and non-steam locomotive manufacturers alike. The former received from BR orders for some 1150 main line diesels, which were divided thus:

Robert Stephenson & Hawthorns (Darlington),	160
North British Locomotive Co,	164
Beyer, Peacock & Co,	166
Vulcan Foundry,	660

The English Electric Co at its Newton-le-Willows and Darlington plants received the lion's share of these orders, which included the 22 3300HP Co-Co 'Deltics' in the early 1960s and 50 2750HP Class 50 Co-Cos in the late 1960s, which proved outstanding performers.

Less happy was the brief history of the diesel hydraulic locomotives produced by NBL and BP for the Western Region. These in the event suffered an early demise, not least due to a BR motive power rationalisation policy and overall declining traffic levels. The bonanza period was all over by 1969.

North British had gone into voluntary liquidation in April 1962, having last made a modest profit in 1955, after which it had plunged deeper into the red. The last diesel left the former Stephenson's plant in Darlington just two years later, and Beyer, Peacock handed over its last diesel locomotive to BR without any ceremony whatever in July 1966. The last locomotives were built, for export, at the former Vulcan Foundry in 1970, since when the works has produced diesel engines for the Ruston group.

With the exceptions of the Hunslet Engine Company and Andrew Barclay & Co, which joined forces in 1972 to form Hunslet Barclay, the remaining small locomotive builders all disappeared during the 1960s. As these lines are being written in late 1998, just a century after the Locomotive Famine, described in Chapter 3, new diesel locomotives are being imported by one of the new privatised railways from North America, but for very different reasons. At the close of the 20th century, the British locomotive industry as such virtually no longer exists.

SOURCES

By the closing years of the 20th century few British former steam locomotive building factories remained. Of those which still existed the heavy plant and equipment for cutting, rolling and flanging steel plate had long since been removed. The construction of a (modified) replica Peppercorn Class A1 4-6-2 in the 1990s has been a special project occupying several years, whereas the production of the 49 originals nearly half a century earlier was a routine operation which could have been undertaken then by any one of about a dozen different British establishments from Southampton to Glasgow in a matter of months.

Happily an extensive archive from Britain's railway works and private locomotive builders survives. For instance many hundreds of glass plate photographic negatives and thousands of working drawings on linen, relating to the activities of (mainly English) railway works are held by the National Railway Museum at York. The records of private industry are more widely scattered. Most complete for any one builder are those of Beyer, Peacock & Co, appropriately accessible in Manchester. The (incomplete) records of the largest enterprise, the North British Locomotive Company and its constituents are largely divided between Glasgow and York. The most lamentable omission is the

paucity of any significant records from Kitson & Co, much of which were reputedly destroyed in 1938 at the behest of a then leading figure in the British locomotive industry. Much of what does remain is largely as a result of accidents of history, fortuitous or otherwise, and is summarised at the end of this chapter. In some cases the quantities of material involved are enormous and are not necessarily catalogued down to the last item on account of limited staff resources at the centre in question.

Two manufacturers produced house journals for limited periods. Beyer, Peacock & Co published the remarkably lavish *Beyer Peacock Quarterly Review* between 1927 and 1932, whose outlook was by no means confined to the products of the Gorton Foundry. *Vulcan Magazine* was published by the Vulcan Foundry between 1948 and 1962. This was more introspective, and included a remarkable series of articles published over several years which described in considerable detail the procedures involved from preliminary estimation to despatch to the customer.

Entry in North British Locomotive Company order book for special light axleload 3ft 6in gauge 2-10-4 for the South African Railways, June 1936.
/NRM

101.

Order No.	Date Ordered.	Branch.	By Whom Ordered.	Description of Engine.	Due Date of Delivery.	Actual Date of Delivery.
	1936					
L899	June 12/15	H P	South African Railways & Harbours. (per Reunert & Lenz) 29/7/36 Supply a fit "NBL" type Mechanical Stoker at extra of £664/-/- 12/8/36 Bd Tender with CS guides & CI Shoes to Coalbunker £50 extra	Contract No 2/1/2453 One Locomotive Engine & Tender, Class 21, 2-10-4 type, 3'6" gauge, 24"x26" cylinders, 4'6" dia coupled wheels 2-8-2 type Tender (10 tons coal & 6000 gals water capacity). Engine to have Std 3B type boiler with plates of nickel steel, superheater, Walschaert Valvegear. Skefko Roller Bearings fitted to leading & trailing bogie axleboxes of engine & to all tender axleboxes. To Specn No L75 & drawings, our offer 6th April 1936.	36 weeks from receipt of drawings & full instructions ie from 11/9/36 due 21/5/37	1937 July 10 11/11/36

110

ENGINE. O-3306

Date issued		DRAWING No.	

CYLINDERS—*continued.*

18·6·08.	Adjustable Crank for Driving Auto. Lub.??	S-1215	N
6·6·08	Lubricator—Drop (details) Auto. Klingers.		
15-4·08	do do Elbow &c	08-7573.	✓
27-5-08	Drain cocks	06-6693	M. ✓
	do Nipple Elbow in Cyl.	06-6978	M. ✓
	Drain cocks arrangement	08-7530	
27·5·08	„ „ details	08-7569.	N ✓
	Bolts and studs See Page 14.		
25-3-08.	Rotary Valve & Liner	07-7315	N ✓
25-3-08	Exhaust Pipe Elbow & Flanges	08-7500	N ✓
7-4-08	„ Tee „ + Stuffing Boxes	08-7501	N ✓
	„ Elbow to S'box.		
29-3-08	Steam Elbow to Cyl.	08-7499	N ✓
27-3-08	„ Tee to Cyl. with Stuffing Box.	08-7498	N ✓
2-4-08	Valve Shafts & crank	08-7512	N.
1-4-08	„ Couplings & drivers.	07-7318	N ✓
14-5-08	Relief Valve	3-1213	N. ✓
25-5-08	Forced Lubricator Nipples in Cyl.	05-6265	M.
1-6-08	do Unions + Back press. Vlv.	3-1116.	M.
	Plugs for Indicator Boxes.	05 6268.	✓

WHEELS, AXLES, AND AXLE BOXES :—

	WHEELS.—Leading. diam. 5'-4" on tread	07-7250	N ✓
	„ Intermediate Driving. diam. 5'-4" „ „	07-7250	N ✓
	„ Trailing. diam. 5'-4" - -	07-7250	N ✓
Jan.1·08.	„ Bogie. diam.	05-6137.	M.A ✓
Nov.6·07	„ Counterweights	07-7348.	N ✓

An extract from the Derby drawing schedule for the experimental Paget Midland Railway 2-6-2 No 2299 completed in 1909, which eluded description in the *contemporary* technical press.   /NRM

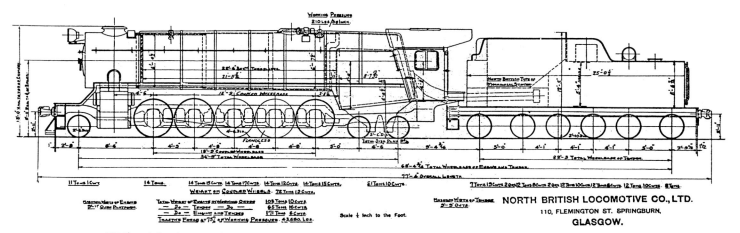

NBL weight diagram for SAR 2-10-4, delivered 13 months after the order was placed. The engine was intended as an alternative to articulated Garratts, but the CME in question retired and his successor favoured 4-8-2 + 2-8-4s instead, no doubt to Beyer, Peacock's delight!   /NRM

An extract from Nasmyth Wilson's specification book showing the remarkable 106 ton 2-10-2T supplied in 1922 to the Bombay Port Trust. Almost forty years later a new boiler was ordered for one of these.   /NRM

1922.

1357.

LOCO. NO. _1357-8_ ~~TEN. NO~~

BOMBAY PORT TRUST.

Gauge _5' 6"_

Owners' Numbers _25, 26_

Negative Nos. _1357, 1357A, B, C, D._

Remarks _NEW_

Working Pressure _180_ lbs. per square inch.		
CYLINDERS (_OUTSIDE._) Diameter	_23½_ inches.	
Stroke	_26_ inches.	
WHEELS. Diameter of Coupled Wheels	_4_ ft.	_3_ in.
" " Bogie "	_3_ ft.	_7_ in.
" " " "	ft.	in.
Wheel Base. Rigid	_19_ ft.	_8_ in.
" " Total	_34_ ft.	_8_ in.
BOILER. Smallest Diameter inside	_6_ ft.	_0_ in.
Length of Barrel	_13_ ft.	_0_ in.
FIRE BOX " Outside	_9_ ft.	_0_ in.
HEATING SURFACE. Fire Box	_183_ square feet.	
" " Tubes	_2115_ " "	
Total	_2298_ " "	
GRATE AREA	_32.3_ square feet.	
TANK CAPACITY	_2500_ gallons.	
FUEL "	_135_ cubic feet.	

DUTY.

LOAD EXCLUSIVE OF ENGINE. (_STARTING_)

On a level _1445_ tons.

On an incline of one per cent. _715_ "

" " two " _135_ " tons.

Mean Tractive Force with mean pressure of ~~100~~ lbs. per square inch. _38007 LBS._ _30.6 M.P.H._ AT _200_ R.P.M.

Speed _35_ miles per hour at Piston Speed of 1,000 feet per minute. RATIO OF ADHESION _4.93_

Curve _405 FT._ Radius.

WEIGHTS.

	F. BOG. T. C. Q	LEAD. T. C. Q.	1st INTER. T. C. Q.	DRIVING T. C. Q.	2nd INTER. T. C. Q.	TRAIL T. C. Q.	H. BOGIE T. C. Q.	TOTAL. T. C. Q.	
	10-9-0	16-0-0	16-15-0	16-17-0	17-8-0	16-16-0	11-8-2	105-12-2	WEIGHT IN FULL WORKING ORDER.
	10-8-0	14-18-0	14-13-2	15-9-0	15-8-0	14-0-2	8-10-2	93-7-2	BOILER FULL, TANK AND BUNKER EMPTY.
	8-13-0	13-11-0	13-9-0	14-4-0	13-19-0	12-18-0	6-13-0	83-7-0	WEIGHT EMPTY.

WEIGHING CONDITIONS.

Water in Boiler (_calculated_) _8 T. 14 C. 0 Q._ _½ GLASS._

Fuel on Grate _8_ cwts.

~~Sand~~ "

Men _3_ "

Water in Tank _11 T. 5 C. 0 Q._

Fuel in Bunker _60_ cwts.

~~TENDER.~~

No. of Wheels Diameter of Wheels = ft. in.

Water = Gallons. Fuel = cubic feet

WEIGHTS.

T. C. Q.	T. C. Q.	T. C. Q.	TOTAL. T. C. Q.	
				WEIGHT IN FULL WORKING ORDER
				WEIGHT EMPTY.

WEIGHING CONDITIONS.

Water T. C. Q.

Fuel T. C. Q.

DRAUGHTSMAN

D. Derbyshire

Cab arrangement photograph of Great Central Railway four cylinder express passenger 4-6-0 locomotive No 1167 *Lord Farringdon*, 1917.
NRM/GOR 157

All manufacturers produced well illustrated brochures promoting their products, an extensive collection of which is held by the National Railway Museum Library & Archive. Most notable in this regard was the Beyer Garratt catalogue produced by Beyer, Peacock & Co in 1947 at a time of national austerity and paper shortages. Hard-backed and printed on heavy art paper this scarcely reflected those difficult times. The author could scarcely believe his good fortune to receive one from the builders in 1962 for the outlay of a (3d) postage stamp!

The Public Record Office at Kew, and the Scottish Record Office in Edinburgh, hold the primary records, including the board minutes, of the English and Welsh, and Scottish main line railways respectively. These will thereby contain entries regarding the establishment and re-equipment of railway works, and orders placed upon them.

A potentially very rich secondary source for sectional general arrangement drawings of locomotives for the British home and overseas market was the contemporary technical press. The reader is referred to *The Engineer* (1856 -), *Engineering* (1864 -), and *The Railway Engineer* (1880 - 1935) in particular. Similar material was also published less frequently in *The Locomotive Magazine* (1896 - 1959) and *The Railway Gazette* (1905 -). All these journals are held in the National Railway Museum Library & Archive at York, which holds a guide to specific references for British and Irish locomotives.

Table 1

Date 1922	Dg No	Full Description of Drawing	Other Information	Drawer No	Class	Name of Draughtsman
Feb 14th	9919	Arrangement of Oil fired boiler (Merryweather)	Electric Passenger Loco	34	4-6-4	L. A. Jones
Feb 14th	9920	Support for Wood Beam	Experimental Vehicle (Bevel Drive)			J. Baty
" 25	9921	Spring Bracket & Details			S3	F. W. Blades
Feb 24th	9922	Experimental Vehicle	Bevel Drive			J. Baty
March 3rd	9923	Arrangement & details for Oil fired boiler	Experimental purposes only	34	Electric 4-6-4	R. H. Jones
March 5th	9924	Cast Steel Saddle for Smokebox	4-6-2 Express Passenger Loco	6		J. Baty
" "	9925 9926	Pipe rack	4-6-4 Electric Pass Loco			H. Hinchcliffe
" "	9926	Footplate Support	4-6-2 Express Pass. Loco	10	4-6-2	J. Baty
" 6th	9927	Footplate Support	" "	10	4-6-2	J. Baty
" 8th	9928 9925	Footplate Support	" "	10	4-6-2	J. Baty
" 9th	9929	Axlebox Guides	" "	20	4-6-2	J. Baty
" 10th	9930	Hornclip D.I.T.	" "	20	4-6-2	J. Baty
" 11th	9931	6'8" coupled wheels	" "	21	4-6-2	J. Baty
" 17th	9932	Pad for Washout Plugs		2	T3 S3	Wm Anderson
" 20th	8933	Outside Motion Plate	" "		4-6-2	F. W. Blades
" 22nd	9934	Arrangement of Lubricating Pipes on Trailing	Axlebox	18	S3	W. Richmond, W. Anderson
" 22nd	9935	Modification of Cab front plate No 2 end	to accommodate oil fired boiler	34	Elect Pass	R. H. Jones
" 23rd	9936	Stand for Westinghouse Pumps		11	4-6-2	J. Baty
" 23rd	9937	Inside Motion Plate		10		F. W. Blades
" 24th	9938	Crank Axle		10	4-6-2	J. Baty
" "	9939	Straight Axle		10	4-6-2	J. Baty
" "	9940	Worn Tyre Sections		31	Z.O.A. 901	E. Kelso
" "	9941	Angle Bar Carriages			4-6-2	F. W. Blades
" 27th	9942	Bogie Axle	4-6-2 Express Pass. Loco			H. Hinchcliffe
" "	9943	Davies & Metcalfe No 9 Loco Exhaust Steam	Injector Class F. Latest Improved Type			L. A. Stokoe
" 28th	9944	Trailing Axle (Radial)	4-6-2 Express Pass Loco			J. S. Tulloch
" "	9945	Trailing Wheel	4-6-2 Express Pass. Loco			J. S. Tulloch
" "	9946	Sketch of an 6 thr Patent 1½ × 1" Lock Nuts				L. A. Stokoe
" 31st	9947	Bogie Axle box Guides	4-6-2 Express Pass Loco			H. Hinchcliffe

Table 2

Drawing No.	Description	Scale	Drawer No	Order No.	Ry. Co.	Remarks	Draughtsman	Date
15720	Sketch of 0-6-0 Side Tank for the War office	4' = 1 foot				Enquiry	Edgar H. Fay	9-3-22
15721	Blow off Cock	F.S.	102	E116	B.N.R.		J. Golightly	14-2-22
15722	Copper Firebox Tubeplate	1½" = 1 ft		D2528	M.R.Co. (West Australia)	Ordering Neg	J. Ll. Owen	14-2-22
15723	Steel Throat & Smokebox Tube Plate	3" = 1 ft	184	D2528	M.R.Co.		J. Ll. Owen	14-2-22
15724	Proposed Hemispherical Int. Drawbar	3" = 1 ft			Madras & S.M.	Standard 0-6-0 Engine	H. Windale	14-2-22
15725	Steel Firebox Plates	1½" = 1-0	184	D2529	Yorkshire Eng Co		F. G. Wade	20-2-22
15726	Driving and Trailing Wheels	4-3-45-1/4	39	D2530	Cavan & Leitrim		G. P. Bateman	25-2-22
15727	Coupling Rods	Full Size	76	D2530	Cavan & Leitrim		G. P. Bateman	24-2-22
15728	Sketch of 4-8-0 Tender Eng for Uganda Ry Enquiry	½" = 1 foot			Uganda Ry	Enquiry	Edgar H. Fay	30-3-22
15729	Copper Firebox Tube Plate	1½" = 1 ft	184	D2532	Grassmoor Colliery	Loco No. 2524	W. J. Southern	16-2-22
15730	Clothing Arr	½" = 1-0	129	E116	B.N. Ry		H. Dearing	30-1-22
15731	Electric Headlight Switches and Dimmer	F.S.	86	E116	B.N.R.	Ordering Neg	J. Golightly	15-2-22
15732	Reversing Shaft & Balance Weight	F.S.	86	D2530	Cavan & Leitrim		G. A. Cox	24-2-22
15733	Connecting Rod	F.S. 1½-1-0	75	D2530	Cavan & Leitrim		F. G. Wade	3-3-22
15734	Handrails	½ & F.S.	65	E116	B.N.R.		H. Dearing	8-2-22
15735	Eccentric Pulleys & Straps	Full Size	78	D2532	Grassmoor Colliery		F. G. Wade	15-2-22
15736	Reversing Rod & Front Hand Cover	F.S.	66	D2532			G. A. Cox	23-2-22
15737	Articulated Engine & Tender Coupling	3" = 1 ft				As applied to M&SM 0-6-0 Engine	H. Windale	24-2-22
15738	Smokebox Tube Plate, Exhaust & Steam Pipes etc	F.S. 3" = 1ft	60	D2532	Grassmoor Colliery		J. Llewellyn Owen	24-2-22
15739	Foundation Ring	F.S. & 3" = 1-0	182	D2532	Grassmoor Colliery		F. G. Wade	27-2-22
15740	Connecting Rod	F & F.S.	75	D2532	" "		G. A. Cox	28-2-22
15741	Crosshead & Slidebars	F.S. & 3" = 1-0	72	D2532	" "		F. G. Wade	3-3-22
15742	Arrangement of Blue Cleaner & Inj. bellow Pipes	1" = 1-0	196	E116 (East Eng)	B.N.R.		G. Mawry	3-3-22
15743	Proposed Bogie for Pipe Line	F.S.	76		Bombay Municipality Lonsa Sale	H. Windale	6-3-22
15744	Coupling Rods	F.S. & 1½ = 1 ft	76	D2532			J. Golightly	8-3-22
15745	Boiler with Belpaire Box				Darjeeling Himalayan. Enquiry	H. Dearing	8-3-22
15746	Steam Set Piece over Green Litter Grate	Full Size	59	D2532	Grassmoor Colliery		J. Llewellyn Owen	9-3-22
15747	Profile of proposed 2-8-0 3 Engine in	½" = 1 ft			Roumanian Railways (for shipping)	G. P. Bateman	12-3-22
15748	Valve Rod Guide & Rev Shaft Brkt	Full Size	83	D2532	Grassmoor Coll		J. Llewellyn Owen	16-3-22

TABLE 20 — British Railway Works, Primary Sources

Works	Negatives (*Register available)		Drawings	Drawing Registers
Crewe	Y	1866-1935*	Y	Y 1890-1943
Nine Elms Eastleigh		c.1885-1943	Y	Y 1885-1958
Cowlairs	Y	c.1920	E	—
Swindon	Y	c.1890-1970	Y	Y 1870-1965
St Rollox	Y	c.1890-1924	E	E 1850-1938
Horwich	Y	1889-1933* 1948-1979*	Y	—
Gateshead Darlington	Y	c.1885-1961	Y	Y 1883-1964
Derby	Y	c.1880-1960	Y	Y 1873-1956
Stratford	Y	c.1890-1952	Y	—
Brighton	Y	c.1905-1922 1940-1958	Y	Y 1870-1967
Ashford			Y	Y 1874-1943
Kilmarnock	Y	(c.1922-1924)	E	E 1873-1923
Gorton	Y	c.1890-1910	Y	Y 1859-1963
Bow	Y	c.1890-1910	Y	—
Doncaster	Y	1896-1967*	Y	Y 1876-1968
Stoke		—	Y	—
Inverness		—	E	—
Melton Constable	Y	(c.1890-1920)	Y	Y 1883-1936

TABLE 21 — Surviving Records of British Locomotive Builders

A. BUSINESS RECORDS

A Barclay, Sons & Co	U	1837-1970
W Beardmore & Co	U	1864-1976
Beyer, Peacock & Co	B	1854-1966
J Fowler & Co	F	c.1860-1940
Neilson & Co	U	1843-1903
North British Loco Co	U	1903-1965
R Stephenson & Co	Y	1823-c.1860
Vulcan Foundry	M	1864-1968
Yorkshire Engine Co	S	1888-1940
Locomotive Manufacturers Association	Y	1875-1965

B. ORDER BOOKS, NEGATIVES AND PHOTOGRAPHS

Builder	Order Books (Specification Books†)		Negatives	Photographs
Avonside Engine Co	L	(Y*)		-
A Barclay & Co	U	(Y*)	G	
W G Bagnall Ltd Order Books	Y 1876-1961			
W Beardmore		-	U 1920s	
Beyer, Peacock & Co	B 1854-1966	(Y*)	B 1855-1966	B 1855-1966
Dübs & Co	Y 1866-1903	†	G 1866-1903	
J Fowler & Co	F c.1860-1940		F c.1860-1940	F c.1860-1940
Hawthorn Leslie & Co	Y 1830-1937		H	Y
Hudswell Clarke & Co	L 1858-1970	(Y*)	-	-
Hunslet Engine Co	L 1864-1970	(Y*)	-	-
Kerr Stuart & Co	L 1892-1930	(Y*)	-	-
Kitson & Co		-	-	Y, (SLS)
Manning Wardle Ltd	L 1858-1928	(Y*)		
Nasmyth Wilson & Co	Y 1839-1938†		B 1920s-1930s	
Neilson & Co	Y 1864-1903		G 1865-1903	
North British Loco Co	G 1903-1961 Y 1903-1947	(Y*)	G 1903-1962	G 1903-1962
Peckett & Co	Y 1881-1958		Y (from IRS)	-
Sharp Stewart & Co	Y 1885-1886 G 1887-1903	(Y*)	G c.1860-1903	
R Stephenson & Co	Y 1825-1937		M 1902-1937	-
R Stephenson & Hawthorns Ltd	Y 1937-1962		M 1937-1956	
Vulcan Foundry	Y 1845-1864 M 1864-1885	(Y*)	M 1866-1956	
Yorkshire Engine Co	S 1866-1956 S 1866-1964	(Y*)		S 1865-1952

IRS = Industrial Railway Society
SLS = Stephenson Locomotive Society

C. DRAWINGS

	Registers	General Arrangement	Detail Working
Avonside Engine Co	L 1885-1934	L	L
A Barclay & Co	U	U	U
Beyer, Peacock & Co	B 1854-1965	B 1854-1965	B 1854-1965
Dübs & Co	G ? -1903	Y 1865-1903	-
J Fowler & Co		F 1860-1903	F 1860-1930
Fox Walker & Co	Y		
Hawthorn Leslie & Co	Y 1871-1937	Y -	Y
Hudswell Clarke & Co	L 1860-1958	L	L
Hunslet Engine Co	L 1864-1939	L	L
Kerr Stuart & Co	L 1890-1930	L	L
Manning Wardle Ltd	L 1883-1925	M 1863-1926	L
Nasmyth Wilson & Co	-	Y 1917-1936	-
Neilson & Co	G ? -1903	Y 1855-1903	-
North British Loco Co	U 1903-1962	Y 1903-1910 U 1903-c.1956	U 1903-c.1956
Peckett & Sons	Y 1882-1960	Y 1882 - c1955	Y 1882-1960
Sharp, Stewart & Co	G ? -1903	Y 1844-1903	-
R Stephenson & Co	Y 1902-1937	M 1902-1937	-
R Stephenson & Hawthorns Ltd	Y 1937-1962	M 1937-1956 Y 1937-1956	Y 1937-1956
Vulcan Foundry	Y 1934-1963	M 1833 -1956 Y 1935-1956	Y 1935-1956
Yorkshire Engine Co		S 1865-1939	-

Drawing office registers provided a wealth of detailed information, and often survive whereas the drawings to which they refer do not. Those originating in a railway works were distinctly 'incestuous' compared to those from a contract builder, as the latter was concerned with highly diverse orders for complete locomotives and spares. To illustrate the contrast are two contemporaneous extracts dating from early 1922 both from Darlington:-

UPPER

The (Gateshead)/Darlington Works drawing registers (two volumes), contain over 17,000 entries between 1883 and 1964. In early 1922 design work on the NER three-cylinder 4-6-2 was rapidly proceeding. At any given time the design office might contain about a dozen draughtsmen, some of their names appeared for decades, eg from the 1910s to the 1940s! */NRM*

LOWER

The Robert Stephenson & Co drawing registers (four volumes) contain nearly 37,000 entries between 1902 and 1963. In early 1922 the design office was concerned with orders from India, and spares for the narrow gauge Cavan & Leitrim Railway in Ireland. Note the 2-8-0 enquiry from Romania, also responded to by NBL in Glasgow. */NRM*

APPENDIX 1

GENERAL REMARKS ON INSPECTION OF LOCOMOTIVES UNDER CONSTRUCTION AT A CONTRACTOR'S WORKS

R C BOND, February 1928

The purpose of inspection during manufacture at a Contractor's Works is to ensure that the locomotive shall be built strictly in accordance with the Specification and drawings and the Railway Company's general standard of workmanship and shop practice. It is difficult to include every detail relating to the Railway Company's standard practice in a specification and drawings may not always be complete in this respect and it is therefore essential for the inspector to have a very full and detailed knowledge of the locomotives he is called upon to inspect. He should be sufficiently conversant with the design of the engines and with the Company's standard practice to be able to draw attention to any omissions in the specification and drawings, and when required to do so, to give full information to the Contractor upon any doubtful points which may arise.

The inspector, must from the very beginning of the contract insist on the highest possible standard of workmanship throughout, with due regard to the conditions under which the locomotives will be required to work. The standard to be aimed at and the end to which all inspection should be directed is for the engines to be able to go into traffic and do their work without giving any trouble whatever which could be attributed to faulty workmanship or inefficient inspection. It is therefore evident that great attention must be given to all points which past experience has shown may lead to trouble or failure in service. In this connection experience in running sheds and on the footplate is invaluable to an inspector, not only from the point of view of knowing where trouble is likely to occur in service but also as a means of becoming familiar with the conditions under which locomotives work.

Special attention must be given to the first engine of every contract to see that it is built absolutely in accordance with the required standards, so that the contractor may know exactly what is required at the earliest possible moment and it will usually (though not always) be found that when once the required standard of workmanship has been set, there will be no great difficulty in maintaining it throughout an order.

The inspector must take pains to gain the complete confidence and respect of the management, foremen and men with whom he is working so that all questions upon which any doubt may exist will immediately be brought to his notice for a decision. While his first duty is firmly to insist on the highest quality of workmanship, an inspector must always be reasonable and he should be and usually is regarded as being of definite assistance to the management of the works which he visits.

An inspector must have no hesitation in rejecting bad work when necessary, but on the other hand, nothing is gained by needless scrapping of work for minor defects which can have no detrimental effect on the locomotive in service. In such cases or where a contractor has made some small and not vital mistake, the inspector may by reason of his experience of repairing and running of locomotives feel justified in allowing the part to be used or suggest means whereby the defect can be remedied. Where any reasonable doubt exists in cases of this kind or upon any other matter arising in the course of his work, the inspector should immediately bring the facts of the case to the notice of headquarters for a decision.

ARRANGEMENT OF WORK

It is quite impossible for an inspector to see every part of each engine in a works of any size turning out more than about one engine per week and the work must therefore be sub-divided and so arranged that in the case of certain parts, such as boilers, frames, cylinders, wheels and axles, etc. every one is thoroughly inspected for each engine throughout the order.

The following inspection work must be carried out for each and every engine throughout an order:-

Engine	Boiler:	Hydraulic Test
		Steam Test
	Firebox:	Examination of stays
		Examination of large tube ferrules

Cylinders: Hydraulic Test

Valve Motion
Piston Valves
Connecting Rods
Coupling Rods
Coupled Wheels Complete
Bogie Wheels
Engine Frames and Slide Bars
Bogie Frames

All Axleboxes in horn blocks
Bedding of axleboxes
Bedding of Big Ends

Setting of chimney and blast pipe

Tender: (or Tanks)
    Tender or Side Tanks: Water Test
    Tender Frames
    Wheels and axles complete
    Axleboxes in horn blocks
    Bedding of axleboxes

Engine and Tender Complete:
    Steam Test:
    Complete test on Mechanical Lubrication for Cylinders and Axleboxes

    Final inspection before delivery

ROBERT STEPHENSON & CO., LIMITED, DARLINGTON.

Somerset & Dorset Joint Railway 2-8-0 No 90 poses with a 6ft tall bowler-hatted man, for its maker's official portrait.

APPENDIX 2

INSPECTION OF SOMERSET & DORSET JOINT RAILWAY 2-8-0S NOS. 86-90, BUILT BY ROBERT STEPHENSON & CO, DARLINGTON 1925 (FROM R C BOND NOTEBOOK, NRM, YORK)

	No.86	No.87	No.88	No.89	No.90
Copper firebox	10 March	18 March	25 March	1 April	7 April
Cylinders (hydraulic)	31 March	2 April	28 April	27 May	4 June
Superheater header	7 April	21 April	5 May	6 May	18 May
Boiler (hydraulic)	8 May	18 May	25 May	11 June	18 June
Boiler (steam)	8 May	18 May	25 May	12 June	19 June
Main frames	21 May	5 June	12 June	22 June	30 June
Coupled wheels	25 May	27 May	27 May	27 May	27 May
Connecting rods	27 May	27 May	12 June	12 June	18 June
Coupling rods	27 May	4 June	12 June	12 June	12 June
Valve motion	5 June	12 June	23 June	30 June	9 July
Engine steam test	5 June	12 June	23 June	30 June	9 July
Tender (complete)	4 June	4 June	18 June	30 June	14 July

Nos. 86-89 entered traffic, July 1925, No. 90 in August 1925. No 86 was exhibited at the Stockton & Darlington Railway Centenary celebrations at Darlington prior to delivery.

APPENDIX 3

Preamble and Conclusion of Specification for Caledonian Railway '191' class 4-6-0 for Callander - Oban line (1922)

THE CALEDONIAN RAILWAY COMPANY 4 - 6 - 0 EXPRESS PASSENGER ENGINE GENERAL STIPULATIONS

The following Specifications, with accompanying Print of General Drawing, are considered sufficiently explicit for the Contractors to make their estimate from, but they will have to work to any Drawings, Gauges, or Templates the Locomotive Superintendent may think desirable to supply; and it is to be understood that the Engines and Tenders are to be manufactured of the best materials of their respective kinds throughout, and fitted and furnished in every respect kinds throughout, and fitted and furnished in every respect in the most complete and workmanlike manner at the expense of the Contractor, and to the satisfaction of the Company's aforesaid Locomotive Superintendent, who will have the power to inspect the work during its progress in building, either himself or by deputy, and to reject any material or workmanship he may consider imperfect.

The said Locomotive Superintendent, before the work is proceeded with, will have the power to amend or alter anything he may think proper; and all disputes that may arise in connection with the building of the Engines shall be referred to and decided by him, and his decision shall be final and binding.

The Contract is not to be sub-let, or any part thereof; and no portion of the work is to be done excepting in the Contractor's Works unless where otherwise specified, or the permission in writing of the Company's Locomotive Superintendent obtained.

These engines to be made in accordance with Drawing, so that the whole of their parts may be duplicates of each other. This must be strictly adhered to. Any duplicate parts not interchangeable will be rejected. No alterations must be made in the general or detailed drawings without the sanction in writing of this Company's Locomotive Superintendent.

Should the Contractor fail to comply with any of the terms of this Specification, the Company retain the power of rejecting the whole or any number of the engines contracted for.

Detail drawings will be supplied to the Contractor, but will not be supplied to firms tendering. For this purpose, if desired, they can be seen at the offices of the Locomotive Department, 130 Springburn Road, St Rollox, Glasgow.

No advantage is to be taken of any omission in the Specification or drawings, as the Contractor may obtain on application to the Locomotive Superintendent a full explanation of any part of the work not sufficiently shown, detailed, or understood.

All material to be manufactured in accordance with the Caledonian Railway Company's standard Specifications, copies of which are supplied.

All tests, whether chemical or mechanical, required by this Company's Locomotive Engineer, including both the cost of material and the preparation of the same for testing, must be made at the expense of the Contractor.

All royalties and patent rights to be paid by Contractor. Contractors must state in what time after receipt of the order they will be prepared to commence delivery, and at what period thereafter they will complete the order, and in the event of the engines not being delivered at the time, and in the numbers stated, this Company reserves the right of delaying payment.

The engines to be delivered, free of charge, at the Company's Works, Saint Rollox, Glasgow, and the Contractor

Caledonian Railway 4-6-0 No 191 in photographic grey livery for its official portrait, November 1922. (The background was painted out on the glass plate negative to give a white sky effect).

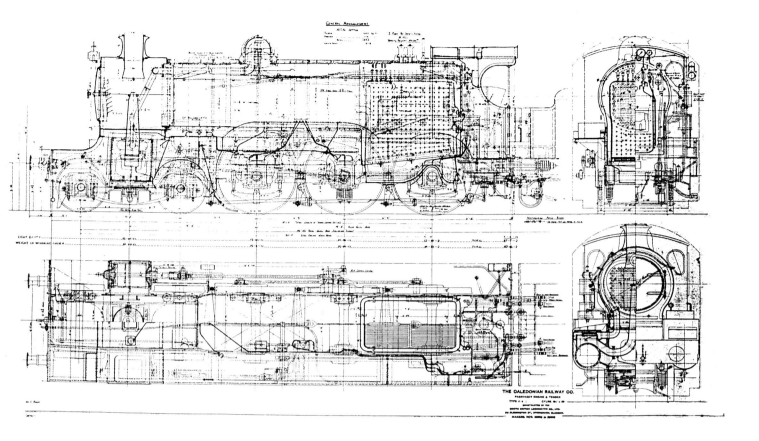

will be held responsible for any defects in them until each has run 2,000 miles, after which they will be inspected by the Company's Locomotive Superintendent, and if they are entirely to his satisfaction he will certify for payment.

Cloth Tracings of the General Drawing of Engine as built, to be supplied simultaneously with the delivery of the first engine, and 12 unmounted photographs, not less than 15 inches by 12 inches of the engine complete, after being specially prepared for photographing.

PATTERNS
All Patterns for Cast Iron, Cast Steel and Brass Work - with the exception of the Wheel Casting patterns - to become the property of the Caledonian Railway Company and delivered along with the last engine of this order.

TENDER
Tenders to be sent to the Secretary of the Caledonian Railway Company, 302 Buchanan Street, Glasgow, on or before.........otherwise they cannot be considered, and to be in the subjoined form and endorsed, "Tender for Locomotives". Drawings sent out with this specification to be signed by Contractor and returned with tender.
The Directors do not bind themselves to accept any tender.

(W Pickersgill)
LOCOMOTIVE SUPERINTENDENT

CALEDONIAN RAILWAY
LOCOMOTIVE DEPARTMENT
ST ROLLOX, GLASGOW
MAY 1922

To the Chairman and Directors of the Caledonian Railway Company

Gentlemen,
We hereby tender to supply Locomotive Engines complete and to deliver them, free of charge, at the works of the Caledonian Railway Company, St Rollox, Glasgow, and in every way in strict conformity with Specifications and Drawings issued by you, dated......at the rate of ....per Locomotive Engine.

NOTE
An order for eight engines and tenders, CR Nos 191-198, was awarded to the North British Locomotive Company on 23 May 1922. They were all delivered from Queen's Park Works between 12 and 30 December 1922 to NBL Order L769, progressive Nos 22955 - 62.

APPENDIX 4A

LOCOMOTIVE PAINTING SPECIFICATIONS

1. MIDLAND RAILWAY 2-4-0 (1875)

The Boiler to receive two coats of Oxalic Paint before being lagged with wood. Frames, Splashers, Handrails, and Weather Screen two coats of Oxalic Paint, and finished with two coats of Green (to sample supplied) and two coats of Varnish. After lagging the Boiler, Frames, Splashers, Handrails, and Weather Screen to have one coat of Lead Color (sic), two coats of Stopping, three coats of Filling up, properly rubbed down, two coats of Lead color (sic), sand papered, two coats of Green to sample, picked out with Black and fine lined with White. Rim of Tyre to be black, inside of Frames and the Axles to be finished with one coat of Vermilion and one of Varnish. Bufferplanks to be finished Vermilion and Varnished. Smokebox, Chimney, back of Firebox, Platforms, Steps, Guards, &c., to be painted Black, two coats inside of Cab to be prepared similar to Boiler and Frame, and finished in Brown and lined.

2. FURNESS RAILWAY 4-6-4T (1918)

Before any painting is done the steel and iron work shall be cleaned, free from scale and rust. The boiler shall receive one coat of boiled oil when warm, and two coats of red oxide paint before being lagged. The lagging plates shall be painted with one coat of red oxide paint, and one coat of lead colour inside. Cab, splashers, side tanks, and coal bunker, lagging plates on boiler, outside frames and wheels shall have two coats of lead colour, stopped with hard stopping, and five coats of filling up, not less than five hours between each coat, then shall be rubbed down, followed by two coats of lead colour faced with pumice stone after each coat, and then to have two coats of Indian red and one of varnish, Indian red. All the painting on outside of engine shall have three coats of the best hard drying body varnish, supplied by firms approved by the Locomotive Superintendent. The frames, smokebox, chimney, firebox casing, ashpan, footplate, brake work, etc., shall have two coats of lead colour and two coats of Japan black. The colouring, picking out, coat of arms, and fine lining shall be same as pattern panel sent by this Company. The inside frames and cross stays shall have two coats of red oxide, and one coat of oak colour to pattern. Front of buffer plates and buffer casing shall be painted vermilion; inside of cab shall have two coats of lead colour, two coats of filling up, rubbed down, and then two coats of oak colour to pattern. The inside of tanks shall be thoroughly cleaned and scoured, shall have two coats of red lead paint, the bottom, sides and rails of coal bunker shall have on coat of lead colour and two coats of Japan black. Gilt letters shall be placed on side tanks, samples of which will be supplied by this Company.

APPENDIX 4B

MIDLAND RAILWAY APPROVED MAKERS OF MATERIALS (1899)

WROUGHT IRON

"Best Yorkshire" Iron must be either from Low Moor, Taylor Brothers, Monk Bridge Iron and Steel Co or Farnley.
RIVETS - Low Moor Iron Rivets from T D Robinson & Co., Derby.

SIEMENS-MARTIN STEEL

BOILER PLATES, FRAME PLATES, and ROOF STAY PLATES from the Leeds Forge Co., Parkgate Iron Co., Butterley Iron Co., John Spencer and Sonjs, or the Steel Company of Scotland.

TYRES AND AXLES from Vickers, Sons and Co., Taylor Brothers, Monk Bridge Iron and Steel Co., or Cammell & Co.

CROSSHEADS, CONNECTING RODS AND STRAPS, SIDE RODS, AND CRANK PINS, from Vickers, Sons & Co., Monk Bridge Iron and Steel Co., Taylor Brothers, Cammell & Co., or John Brown & Co.,

SPRINGS from Thomas Turton & Sons, Cammell and Co., J Brown and Co or Steel, Peech and Tozer.

SPIRAL SPRINGS - Timmis's Patent, from Turton Bros. and Matthews.

CASTINGS from Monk Bridge Iron and Steel Co., Cammell & Co., the Steel Company of Scotland, Firth and Sons, Jessop and Sons, or John Brown & Co.

WHEEL CENTRE CASTINGS from Monk Bridge Iron and Steel Co., Thomas Firth & Sons, Jessop and Sons, or Steel Company of Scotland.

RIVETS - Steel Rivets from T.D. Robinson & Co. Derby.

CRUCIBLE CAST STEEL
PISTON RODS, SLIDE BARS, AND CROSSHEAD PINS from Vickers, Sons and Co., or Thomas Turton and Sons.

COPPER
Plates from Bibby, Son & Co., Vivian & Sons, Neville, Druce & Co., Elliott Metal Co., Williams, Foster & Co., Newton, Keats & Co., Wilkes, Sons, & Mapplebeck, or Thomas Bolton & Sons.
BARS, soft rolled, from Broughton Copper Co.
TUBES from Everett, Broughton Copper Co., Muntz Metal Co., Elliott Metal Co., Wilkes, Sons, & Mapplebeck, Thomas Bolton & Sons, Grice, Grice & Son, or other approved makers.

VARIOUS
STONE'S BRONZE - From J Stone & Co., Deptford.
METALLIC PACKING - Supplied by United Kingdom Metallic Packing Co., Ltd.
RICHARDS' PLASTIC METAL - Supplied by J.H. Richards & Co., Birmingham
INDIA-RUBBER - From G. Spencer, Moulton & Co., Ltd.

APPENDIX 5

LOCOMOTIVE BUILDING STATISTICS

It is impossible to be absolutely *precise* regarding locomotive building statistics. For early manufacturers one often has incomplete secondary sources. Some builders allocated works numbers to tenders, spare boilers and in the case of the Yorkshire Engine Company colliery winding engines and even motor cars. Even for the relatively few 20th century builders it is not straightforward. Beyer, Peacock's order books give trial and despatch dates for each engine, but the corresponding North British Locomotive Company record (sometimes) provides only first and last delivery dates. If any order extends from one year into the next it is virtually impossible to determine how many engines were 'built' in which year, and by built does one mean completed or despatched? Sometimes despatch could be significantly delayed, as in the case of the 2-10-2s for Iran in the early 1950s. Industrial locomotive builders often built engines 'for stock' which might have been constructed a few years before 'immediate' delivery.

Railway and builder's records could beg to differ. For example, as far as Beardmore's were concerned its order for twenty 4-6-0s from the Great Eastern Railway was dated 1920, but the GER itself put the engines into traffic between June 1920 and April 1921. Comparison of Table 4 (Chapter 2) and Appendix 8 illustrate this apparent anomaly for the extreme case of 1848 when more new engines apparently entered service than were actually built.

It is somewhat easier to be accurate in respect to the output of railway works, but then there is the problem of so-called 'renewals', when was an engine new as opposed to being a 'rebuild' for the accountant's benefit? Only strictly new locomotives have been recorded.

A small number of locomotives fell in both camps, eg LNWR 4-6-0s and GNR 2-8-0s, commenced by the railway works and then passed over to a contractor for completion. Conversely of 50 2-6-0s ordered by the GWR from Robert Stephenson & Co c 1919, only 35 were delivered, the balance of 15, although fabricated by the contractor, was actually assembled at Swindon Works. For simplicity therefore *the place of assembly* is deemed to be the criterion. For obvious reasons an exception has to be made for the relatively few imported locomotives, which were delivered in 'knocked-down' form. Railway-built locomotives frequently incorporated 'bought in' parts in any case, and sometimes *vice versa*. On this basis the 50 'Woolwich' 2-6-0s purchased by the Southern Railway have been considered to be railway-built as they were erected by the railway.

Having obtained annual totals, trends are perhaps more important than absolute values, and these can be discerned better by calculating three-year moving averages. These reveal several unmistakeable peaks in locomotive building, which can be readily related to the condition of the contemporary economy and certain other factors, eg wartime, both 1914-18 and 1939-45.

Thus as far as the British domestic railway scene was concerned, the peaks were 1840-41, 1847-48, 1865-67, 1872-75, 1891-92, and 1899-1900. Of these by far the most pronounced was that of 1847-48, which reflected the heavy demand by new railway enterprises which had gained government approval during the so-called 'Railway Mania' of 1844-46. Nearly 1,200 route miles of new railway were opened to traffic in England, Scotland and Wales during 1848 alone, which was by far the greatest ever annual total. Perhaps surprisingly, *in relative terms* the peak of 1899-1900 was not exceptional.

There were no such peaks after 1900, with the possible exception of 1921 taken in isolation (which amounted to a post-war recovery process) mainly because the underlying trend was one of *declining* demand which covered only replacement and no longer net growth. It can also be shown that the average life expectancy of British steam locomotives steadily increased from 1860 onwards.

Initially corresponding peaks can be discerned in British commercial locomotive building, except that there was a marked peak in 1884-85, reflecting a good export trade, which oddly contrasted with the domestic gloom. Conversely, there were no peaks around 1892 or 1899, but there was in 1907, which was not particularly apparent 'at home'. Other export peaks were 1913, 1920, and 1947, in terms of quantity rather than total value.

Not surprisingly an inverse relationship can be discerned between the proportion of locomotives built in railway works in relation to total domestic demand, and by the major private builders for the home railways in relation to their own total production. However, the one factor was not *necessarily* dependent upon the other.

On a decade basis it is interesting to note that just about twice as many steam locomotives were built in Britain during the 1860s than the 1850s, and twice as many in the 1900s than the 1860s. Total production in the 1950s approximated to that in the 1840s.

In addition to the builders specifically referred to in the text were many others, usually with only modest output which had negligible influence on the foregoing statements. These were particularly numerous in the very early years, but after say, 1860, their collective contribution rarely exceeded thirty engines per annum. Such builders, for example, Fletcher Jennings & Co of Whitehaven, Henry Hughes of Loughborough, and C P Markham of Chesterfield had virtually ceased production by the 1920s. The largest in this category would have been Black, Hawthorn & Co of Gateshead (1866-1902) with c. 800 engines, whose final locomotive deceptively carried works number 1215.

Underlying Trends

It is a simple matter to derive formulae which define underlying trends from which the real magnitude of major deviations can be assessed:

1. New locomotives to traffic, British main line railway companies (from all sources):

a) 1830-1895, $= 80 + 9.85y$

b) 1895-1960, $= 720 - 9.85(y - 65)$

2. Annual production by major locomotive builders:
a) 1830-1904, $= 10.95y$
b) 1904-1958, $= 810 - 13.06(y - 74)$

3. Annual exports by major locomotive builders:
a) 1830-1907, $= -70 + 9.5y$
b) 1907-1958, $= 660 - 11.4(y - 69)$

y = number of years after 1830

APPENDIX 6

ESTIMATED ANNUAL STEAM LOCOMOTIVE PRODUCTION OF MAJOR BRITISH LOCOMOTIVE BUILDERS 1831 - 1960

	BP	VF	K	RS	HL	NW	N	SS	D	TOTAL
1831				13	3					16
1832				18	9					27
1833		7		36	0			1		44
1834		2		24	0			3		29
1835	15			13	0			0		28
1836	19			22	3			0		44
1837	9			30	8			10		57
1838	22			39	29			21		111
1839	21			36	9	8		81		155
1840	34	6		46	30	14		37		167
1841	23	0		35	14	8		52		132
1842	16	2		36	3	16		35		108
1843	16	0		35	11	2	7	40		111
1844	5	7		37	17	4	0	30		100
1845	28	11		44	58	11	0	48		200
1846	23	19		84	45	0	20	63		254
1847	47	17		70	34	10	0	99		277
1848	20	23		72	81	12	3	66		277
1849	2	21		67	15	4	7	83		199
1850	0	7		17	21	6	13	25		89

	BP	VF	K	RS	HL	NW	N	SS	D	TOTAL
1851		1	14	41	33	4	0	23		116
1852		8	23	53	33	5	15	24		161
1853		12	26	50	23	6	5	52		174
1854		27	24	56	24	0	9	85		225
1855	20	37	23	53	23	0	25	78		259
1856	25	3	41	48	16	0	6	47		186
1857	25	8	31	60	7	0	22	60		213
1858	27	4	24	51	17	0	27	88		238
1859	33	8	43	45	22	0	86	22		259
1860	51	21	13	67	14	0	53	75		299
1861	65	27	54	89	31	0	63	78		407
1862	84	24	17	57	18	0	60	74		334
1863	66	7	56	73	9	0	110	67		388
1864	86	43	40	78	30	0	38	96	14	425
1865	114	0	27	71	40	0	79	80	21	432
1866	111	26	69	94	37	0	87	102	110	636
1867	80	12	32	40	33	6	24	87	72	386
1868	57	2	31	96	13	0	61	65	42	367
1869	67	0	42	47	2	0	73	79	58	368
1870	90	20	37	62	7	0	78	119	75	488

	BP	VF	K	RS	HL	NW	N	SS	D	TOTAL
1871	103	22	62	36	7	0	95	90	98	513
1872	102	53	39	41	12	15	74	81	92	499
1873	112	28	35	76	21	18	116	105	84	595
1874	123	36	41	66	29	33	109	79	97	613
1875	95	34	58	65	32	7	60	57	111	519
1876	95	33	53	39	12	9	117	105	95	558
1877	101	5	85	18	4	4	161	81	105	564
1878	102	28	51	15	18	2	123	81	100	520
1879	63	12	31	25	3	5	120	53	110	422
1880	91	27	70	27	16	0	117	73	131	552
1881	107	58	53	13	17	11	102	87	102	550
1882	131	56	20	47	5	3	120	42	166	590
1883	144	29	70	46	35	20	160	61	181	746
1884	149	38	126	58	24	26	202	97	160	880
1885	116	63	98	21	23	27	236	97	130	811
1886	132	47	34	2	13	14	113	49	111	515
1887	60	21	70	21	11	25	122	42	100	472
1888	111	9	55	11	13	21	178	64	78	540
1889	142	24	62	14	24	21	123	95	106	611
1890	143	45	53	28	25	23	162	86	158	723
1891	144	22	113	21	30	14	187	108	153	792
1892	101	47	76	6	20	17	136	48	88	539
1893	52	25	29	0	11	6	151	62	146	482
1894	74	22	50	5	6	12	91	76	146	482
1895	57	36	36	10	10	12	112	104	64	441
1896	120	45	32	6	19	29	165	176	171	763
1897	90	39	55	19	10	20	184	118	121	656
1898	102	85	109	38	10	32	185	150	114	825
1899	98	51	58	41	38	19	230	98	142	775
1900	109	76	86	12	28	26	199	111	156	803
1901	109	43	56	19	35	32	221	138	201	854
1902	105	61	61	6	27	28	213	137	103	779
1903	93	57	46	30	18	29	166	42	64	845
							NBL 300			
1904	110	91	99	26	22	18	485			851
1905	119	68	26	40	30	44	**573**			900
1906	142	98	103	56	31	28	520			978
1907	147	95	92	63	55	41	539			**1032**
1908	**152**	120	91	43	20	40	462			928
1909	131	123	80	41	36	41	398			850
1910	116	99	90	26	45	18	289			683
1911	108	84	71	47	50	29	349			738
1912	100	111	55	56	45	29	335			731
1913	110	136	69	52	**59**	39	433			898
1914	99	127	65	59	47	43	400			840
1915	56	75	97	37	71	30	235			601
1916	28	15	0	32	41	18	216			350
1917	1	38	1	32	59	18	294			443
1918	8	12	48	25	27	18	217	**AW**	**B**	355
1919	16	10	5	26	39	20	368	3		487
1920	43	142	80	21	47	37	307	132	74	883
1921	85	108	58	38	53	**47**	240	99	61	789
1922	44	73	6	17	12	23	97	**221**	29	522
1923	34	121	2	20	36	25	143	86	5	472
1924	42	74	22	15	28	32	74	100	36	423
1925	71	150	7	29	18	22	197	109	0	603
1926	59	128	3	16	15	22	156	20	0	419
1927	75	171	12	16	15	25	182	35	20	551
1928	101	74	5	39	45	26	141	117	**134**	682
1929	75	76	16	27	12	28	96	33	0	363
1930	96	110	15	40	12	19	130	86	26	534

	BP	VF	K	RS	HL	NW	NBL	AW	B	TOTAL
1931	41	104	8	18	3	2	41	20	6†	243
1932	12	3	11	0	5	8	0	0		39
1933	32	3	2	0	1	2	16	0		56
1934	6	53	1	37	12	3	83	10		205
1935	9	86	2	8	7	11	74	104		301
1936	34	69	3	29	25	18	106	84		368
1937	46	16	0	29	28	12	43	153†		334
				RSH						
1938	35	36	5†	36		4†	64			180
1939	36	2		6			82			136
1940	36	24		11			71			132
1941	30	4		35			76			145
1942	13	4		22			131			170
1943	47	115		44			312			518
1944	44	205		61			312			622
1945	38	143		44			176			401
1946	42	143		39			206			394
1947	40	119		38			210			407
1948	45	66		53			217			381
1949	45	117		60			238			460
1950	56	93		83			179			411
1951	72	95		62			160			389
1952	46	59		58			140			303
1953	60	55		40			114			269
1954	44	87		46			115			292
1955	56	56		24			61			197
1956	67	2†		15			50			132
1957	66	0		11			20			97
1958	26†	0		5†			4†			35
1959	0	0		0			0			0
1960	0	0		0			0			0

† steam locomotive production ceased

ABBREVIATIONS

MAJOR BUILDERS

BP Beyer, Peacock & Co
VF Vulcan Foundry
K Kitson & Co
RS Robert Stephenson & Co
HL R & W Hawthorn Leslie & Co
NW Nasmyth Wilson & Co
N Neilson & Co
SS Sharp Stewart & Co
D Dübs & Co
NBL North British Locomotive Co
AW Armstrong Whitworth & Co
B W Beardmore & Co
RSH Robert Stephenson & Hawthorns Ltd

MINOR BUILDERS

AE Avonside Engine Co
WGB W G Bagnall Ltd
AB Andrew Barclay, Sons & Co
F John Fowler & Co
HC Hudswell Clarke Ltd
HE Hunslet Engine Co
KS Kerr, Stuart Ltd
MW Manning Wardle Ltd
FW Fox Walker & Co
P Peckett & Co
YE Yorkshire Engine Co

APPENDIX 7

ESTIMATED ANNUAL STEAM LOCOMOTIVE PRODUCTION OF BRITISH INDUSTRIAL LOCOMOTIVE BUILDERS
(EXCLUDING FIRELESS LOCOMOTIVES)
(1855 - 1965)

	AE	WGB	AB	F	HC	HE	KS	MW	P	YE	Total
1855											0
1856											0
1857											0
1858			2								2
1859			1					7			8
1860			3					13			16
1861			1		2			15			18
1862			10		2			30			42
1863			4		3			34			41
1864			4		12			36			52
1865			8		13	4		38			63
1866			10	25	16	10		48		3	112
1867	63		16	39	8	11		1		22	173
1868	30		10	19	3	7		17		41	127
1869	15		7	0	1	8		15		62	108
1870	16		14	10	5	14		37	6	41	143
1871	51		15	11	12	17		47	8	0	161
1872	54		16	27	11	15		38	20	25	206
1873	51		8	3	14	22		48	36	21	203
1874	61		11	11	11	25		46	49	21	235
1875	46		17	7	15	20		61	37	14	217
1876	59	1	7	13	19	19		56	32	37	243
1877	45	4	13	3	6	21		43	28	19	182
1878	23	1	3	1	8	20		36	47	38	177
1879	10	4	14	17	8	18		13		0	84
1880	47	9	10	16	6	22		40		2	152
1881	10	9	18	19	19	21		42	3	4	145
1882	10	7	14	18	12	21		45	1	0	128
1883	10	10	15	28	9	31		50	4	3	160
1884	10	7	10	22	13	24		25	7	5	113
1885	1	13	11	26	13	25		23	9	8	132
1886	0	10	4	14	5	32		40	6	1	112
1887	0	14	6	19	7	29		42	8	1	126
1888	0	11	12	31	21	33		65	7	5	185
1889	1	16	20	26	22	24		40	7	0	146
1890	2	6	22	16	20	25		61	16	3	171
1891	3	11	29	17	21	28	1	30	15	7	176
1892	2	8	11	15	16	19	4	19	6	2	102
1893	5	14	16	9	13	27	7	14	11	0	116
1894	1	15	18	21	12	21	6	15	13	0	122
1895	7	33	12	8	20	21	9	29	11	2	152
1896	10	24	20	13	21	18	12	23	19	8	168
1897	15	27	24	6	12	3	13	32	21	12	165
1898	8	36	29	8	16	28	18	50	34	9	236
1899	14	43	26	1	34	21	31	45	31	3	247
1900	22	37	30	7	36	25	44	43	34	15	293
1901	6	29	26	0	21	27	27	27	33		201
1902	13	39	27	3	33	36	25	0	28	3	257
1903	9	31	38	5	41	36	40	28	27	7	262
1904	28	22	34	1	26	25	31	23	25	8	223
1905	10	18	34	5	37	21	24	30	20	11	215
1906	26	49	25	4	37	37	30	25	27	8	268
1907	12	33	40	17	42	49	42	24	31	16	306
1908	25	10	30	10	26	16	37	12	11	2	179
1909	9	23	28	7	50	29	56	11	10	3	226
1910	20	20	26	4	26	44	42	13	17	2	214
1911	22	18	44	11	37	27	35	18	13	1	226
1912	18	34	42	11	37	20	32	18	33	13	258
1913	24	31	45	3	46	37	23	24	25	17	275
1914	26	25	35	3	45	24	39	26	26	5	254

	AE	WGB	AB	F	HC	HE	KS	MW	P	YE	Total
1915	8	6	39	8	62	23	92	21	29	5	293
1916	26	7	31	8	70	43	50	26	30	4	295
1917	28	28	51	0	65	49	37	25	24	1	308
1918	27	23	46	0	39	37	51	28	20	0	271
1919	17	38	37	1	31	68	47	10	16	1	266
1920	31	20	64	7	35	11	61	14	18	0	261
1921	26	22	37	12	37	16	44	20	10	4	228
1922	12	24	11	5	23	18	16	0	10	3	122
1923	14	20	38	18	19	10	17	11	19	7	173
1924	27	22	35	24	40	24	10	9	25	7	223
1925	16	24	28	12	22	25	40	4	10	7	188
1926	18	21	21	5	9	26	10	4†	18	0	132
1927	12	29	39	13	24	44	36		18	3	218
1928	21	34	15	4	19	47	24		13	6	183
1929	5	26	15	7	19	35	10		10	6	133
1930	11	31	5	3	3	26	20†		7	2	131
1931	14	28	5	0	4	19			21	4	95
1932	3	19	2	0	1	5			4	2	36
1933	10	22	3	1	0	8			9	1	54
1934	0	14	6	6	6	6			14	4	56
1935	1†	20	10	3	4	15			5	1	59
1936		25	6	1†	13	16			16	1	78
1937		4	24		20	24			15	3	80
1938		5	14		12	11			19	0	62
1939		3	17		5	14			11	0	50
1940		11	22		8	21			14	0	76
1941		16	20		6	19			19	1	81
1942		27	29		6	10			9	2	83
1943		15	12		18	45			11	1	92
1944		40	16		21	64			10	0	151
1945		31	14		15	35			7	0	102
1946		22	22		9	19			9	0	81
1947		11	17		8	22			4	3	65
1948		36	16		11	18			12	10	103
1949		27	23		6	19			7	13	9
1950		28	19		8	29			13	16	113
1951		20	20		6	29			6	14	95
1952		18	14		5	27			11	11	86
1953		19	12		10	27			8	9	85
1954		16	17		11	23			7	11	85
1955		2	10		8	22			3	18	63
1956		2	3		0	14			1	8†	28
1957		1†	0		0	2			1		4
1958			0		1	2			1†		4
1959			0		0	2			0		2
1960			0		2	0					2
1961			0		3†	0					3
1962		1†				3					4
1963						0					0
1964						2					2
1965						0					0

Note: 1 final steam locomotive was built by the Hunslet Engine Company in 1971.

† = steam locomotive production ceased.

APPENDIX 8

ESTIMATED PRODUCTION BY CONTRACTORS FOR BRITISH MAIN LINE RAILWAYS, 1831 - 1956
* denotes imports

1831	30	1861	256	1891	222	1921	302
1832	15	1862	151	1892	273	1922	102
1833	12	1863	140	1893	193	1923	10
1834	19	1864	246	1894	133	1924	87
1835	17	1865	312	1895	108	1925	152
1836	29	1866	413+15*	1896	180	1926	212
1837	65	1867	262	1897	213	1927	214
1838	144	1868	191+1*	1898	102+1*	1928	215
1839	183+4*	1869	96	1899	345+55*	1929	107
1840	257+11*	1870	238	1900	366+35*	1930	157
1841	256+2*	1871	277	1901	261+1*	1931	86
1842	167+2*	1872	238	1902	151	1932	5
1843	46	1873	284	1903	104+1*	1933	0
1844	87	1874	284	1904	115	1934	97
1845	224	1875	295	1905	50+2*	1935	209
1846	287	1876	375	1906	63	1936	232
1847	498	1877	169	1907	75	1937	196
1848	546	1878	178	1908	108	1938-41	0
1849	320	1879	92	1909	68	1942	50
1850	155	1880	141	1910	89	1943-45	0
						1946	73
1851	185	1881	214	1911	46	1947	105
1852	163	1882	192	1912	124	1948	96
1853	205	1883	192	1913	67	1949	89
1854	221	1884	202	1914	59+10*	1950	101
1855	209	1885	207	1915	66	1951	62
1856	116	1886	82	1916	53	1952	57
1857	134	1887	59	1917	41	1953	11
1858	86	1888	55	1918	77	1954	18
1859	100	1889	105	1919	68	1955	30
1860	134	1890	140	1920	127	1956	9†

APPENDIX 9

CONTRIBUTION BY RAILWAY WORKS TO BRITISH MAIN LINE RAILWAY STEAM LOCOMOTIVE SUPPLY AND IN RELATION TO TOTAL PRODUCTION BY DECADE, 1831-40 TO 1951-60

Decade	Estimated Production Rly Works (W)	Contractors (C)	Imports	Total (T)	Post-War 'Windfalls'	$\frac{W}{T}$	Major Contractors Production (M)	$\frac{C}{M}$	Minor Contractors Production	Estimated Total Production (rounded)	Proportion of Grand Total
1831-40	0	771	15	786	-	0.00	1038	0.74	0	1250*	0.011
1841-50	434	2586	4	3024	-	0.14	2887	0.90	0	3600*	0.033
1851-60	1084	1553	0	2637	-	0.41	2731	0.57	26	4250*	0.039
1861-70	2587	2305	16	4908	-	0.53	4351	0.53	879	7800*	0.072
1871-80	3731	2333	0	6064	-	0.62	5367	0.43	1860	11200	0.103
1881-90	3866	1448	0	5314	-	0.73	6438	0.22	1418	12000	0.110
1891-00	5702	2135	91	7928	-	0.72	6558	0.33	1777	14250	0.131
1901-10	4304	1084	4	5392	-	0.80	8700	0.12	2351	15400	0.142
1911-20	2572	728	10	3310	54	0.78	6326	0.12	2707	11600	0.107
1921-30	3040	1557	0	4597	379	0.66	5358	0.29	1731	10500	0.097
1931-40	2890	1077	0	3967	-	0.73	1994	0.54	646	5530	0.051
1941-50	2378	413	0	2791	886	0.85	3909	0.11	986	7275	0.067
1951-60	1225	160	0	1385	3	0.88	1714	0.09	454	3400	0.031
Total	33813	18150	140	51963	1322	0.65	57371	0.32	14835	108,000	1.000

* includes numerous short term builders
† excludes fireless locos (161 built 1912 - 1962) and Sentinel locos (c.300 built 1925 - 1958)
('Windfalls' were mainly ex-ROD 2-8-0s after World War 1 and MOS 2-8-0s, 2-10-0s and 0-6-0STs after World War 2)

APPENDIX 10

BRITISH STEAM LOCOMOTIVE EXPORTS

A. Value — average of five year periods, 1855 - 1965

Period	Actual £	At 1913 Price Levels approx £	Period	Actual £	At 1913 Price Levels approx £
1855-59	968,461	830,000	1915-19	1,651,888	929,000
1860-64	940,264	868,000	1920-24	4,748,861	2,591,000
1865-69	922,906	791,000	1925-29	2,932,987	1,731,000
1870-74	793,235	680,000	1930-34	1,360,441	942,000
1875-79	713,138	642,000	1935-39	1,218,812	784,000
1880-84	1,084,868	1,056,000	(1940)	N/A	-
1885-89	1,186,009	1,377,000	1941-45	752,600	376,000
1890-94	1,208,343	1,359,000	(1946)	N/A	-
1895-99	1,168,496	1,402,000	1947-50	6,381,206	2,873,000
1900-04	1,997,276	2,247,000	1951-55	7,554,499	2,640,000
1905-09	2,764,764	**3,017,000**	1956-60	1,787,455	527,000
1910-14	2,554,997	2,555,000	1961-65	8,970	2,400

B. High and low points in British steam locomotive exports (by value)

	PEAKS			TROUGHS	
Year	Actual (£)	(1913)(£)	Year	Actual (£)	(1913)(£)
1907	3,400,000	3,700,000	1918	1,080,000	500,000
1914	3,800,000	3,800,000	1924	1,850,000	1,060,000
1921	7,900,000	3,500,000	1932	370,000	250,000
1950	8,000,000	3,400,000	1942	140,000	70,000

C. Comparative values of locomotive exports 1913, 1930-1938

	UK (£)	GERMANY (£)	USA (£)
1913	2,782,000	2,698,000	N/A
1930	3,751,000	2,852,000	N/A
1931	1,497,000	1,079,000	287,000
1932	367,000	230,000	33,000
1933	734,000	200,000	55,000
1934	453,000	164,000	124,000
1935	891,000	800,000	166,000
1936	1,301,000	706,000	105,000
1937	1,130,000	943,000	266,000
1938	1,715,000	2,630,000	N/A

Note on variations in the value of the Pound Sterling, if the value in 1913 = £1.00, the following equivalents applied

1850	=	£0.97	1930	=	£1.58
1875	=	£1.11	1940	=	£1.83
1900	=	£0.86	1950	=	£2.33
1910	=	£0.94	1960	=	£3.44
1920	=	£2.50	1970	=	£5.14

The last British-built steam locomotive, the 750mm gauge 0-4-2ST (HE 3902) completed by the Hunslet Engine Company in November 1971 for industrial service in Indonesia, where it was photographed in August 1993.
K R Chester

BIBLIOGRAPHY

1. Locomotive Building

British Locomotive Builders, Past and Present, *The Locomotive* **33** (1) April 1927, 130 - 132 (2) May 1927, 163 - 164.

PEP Engineering Reports III, Locomotives Political & Economic Planning, 1951, 75p.

British Steam Locomotive Builders, J W Lowe, Goose & Son, 1975, 704p.

Building Britain's Locomotives, J W Lowe, Moorland Publishing, 1979, -p.

A Short History of American Locomotive Building in the Steam Era, J H White, Bass Inc, 1982, 112p.

Product Proliferation in the British Locomotive Building Industry, 1850 - 1914: An Engineer's Paradise? M W Kirby, *Business History*, **30** (3) July 1988, 287 - 305.

Locomotive Manufacturing, M Rutherford *Backtrack*, (1) **5** (5) September/October 1991, 210 - 216 (2) **6** (4) July/August 1992, 201 - 206 (3) **7** (1) January/February 1993, 12 - 18.

2. British Railway Works

Repair and Production Policy for Locomotives and Rolling Stock, British Transport Commission, 1959.

The Railway Workshops of Britain, 1823 - 1986, E J Larkin & J G Larkin, Macmillan Press, 1988, 266p.

An Illustrated History of British Railways Workshops, E J Larkin, Oxford Publishing Co, 1992, 184p.

Crewe Locomotive Works and its Men, B Reed, David & Charles, 1982, 256p.

North Road Locomotive Works Darlington 1863 - 1966, K Hoole, Roundhouse Books 1967, 102p.

Derby Works and Midland Locomotives, J B Radford, Ian Allan, 1971, 239p.

Horwich Locomotive Works, M D Smith, Wyre Publishing, 1996, 209p.

The Great Western at Swindon Works, A S Peck, Oxford Publishing Co, 1983, 281p.

3. British Locomotive Builders

The First Armstrong Whitworth Locomotive, *The Railway Gazette*, 21 November 1919, 667 - 673.

Armstrong's of Elswick, K Warren, (Chapter 24) Macmillan, 1989.

The Avonside Engine Company of Bristol, M Smithers *Backtrack* **7** (4) July - August 1993, 181 - 7.

Bagnalls of Stafford, A C Baker & T D A Civil, The Oakwood Press, 1973, 110p.

Barclay 150 1840 - 1990, R Wear, Hunslet Barclay Ltd 1990, 96p.

From Howitzers and Field Guns to Locomotives (W Beardmore), *The Railway Gazette*, 24 December 1920, 816 - 821.

Beardmore, the History of a Scottish Industrial Giant, J R Hume & M S Moss, Heineman, 1979, 364p.

Builders For 111 Years (Beyer, Peacock & Co), B Reed, *The Railway Magazine* (1) September 1966, 493 - 497 (2) October 1966, 567 - 570.

Beyer, Peacock Locomotive Builders to the World, R L Hills & D Patrick, The Transport Publishing Company, 1982, 302p.

The Hatcham Ironworks, New Cross: The locomotive works of George England & Co, and its subsequent history, D Perrett & O James, *London's Industrial Archaeology* (3), 1984, 1 - 14.

Power on Land & Sea, a history of R & W Hawthorn Leslie, J F Clarke, Hawthorn Leslie (Engineers) Ltd c. 1978, 118p.

A Hunslet Hundred, L T C Rolt, David & Charles, 1964, 177p.

End of an Era, Hunslet's Steam Locomotive Production, 1949 - 71, D Townsley, *Railway World* (1) May 1987, 277 - 280 (2) July 1987, 413 - 416.

The Hunslet Engine Works, D H Townsley, Plateway Press, 1998.

Kitsons of Leeds 1837 - 1937 E Kitson Clark, Locomotive Publishing Co Ltd, 1938, 185p.

What's in a Name, Kitson's of Leeds, M Rutherford, *Backtrack* 12 (2) February 1998, 97 - 103.

A Very Special Family (Kitson's), E F Clark, *The Railway Magazine*, May 1989, 292 - 297.

Steam from Lowca, I Kyle, Author, 1974 36p.

The New Works of Messrs Nasmyth, Wilson & Co Ltd, Patricroft, Manchester, *The Railway Gazette*, 27 June 1913, 779 - 790.

Nasmyth Wilson & Co Ltd, G S Moore, Arley Hall Publications, undated, 63p.

The North British Locomotive Company between the wars, R H Campbell, *Business History* **20** (2) July 1978, 201 - 234.

Giants of Steam, the full story of the North British Locomotive Co Ltd, R P Bradley, Oxford Publishing Company, 1995, 192p.

The Atlas Works, Glasgow, *The Engineer*, 14 December 1894, 511 - 519.

Peckett's in Retrospect, R A Wheeler, *Industrial Railway Record*, (53), April 1974, 198 - 203.

A Century of Locomotive Building by Robert Stephenson & Co, 1823 - 1923, by J G H Warren, Andrew Reid & Co Ltd, 1923, 461p (Reprinted by David & Charles, 1970).

Forth Banks Works 1823 - 1959, M J Lee, *The Journal of the Stephenson Locomotive Society*, **36** (414) January 1960, 32 - 36.

The Vulcan Locomotive Company's Works at Newton-le-Willows, *The Railway Gazette*, 6 November 1908, 533 - 53 (A-D).

The Vulcan Locomotive Works 1830 - 1930, The Locomotive Publishing Co Ltd, 1930, 122p.

The Railway Foundry Leeds 1839 - 1969 E B Wilson - Hudswell Clarke & Co Ltd, R N Redman, Goose & Son Publishers Ltd, 1972, 206p.

Some Notes on the Yorkshire Engine Company, C B Harley *The Journal of the Stephenson Locomotive Society*, **52** (608) March 1976, 70 - 84.

4. Geographical Studies

Scottish Railways and the Development of Scottish Locomotive Building in the Nineteenth Century, W Vamplew, *Business History Review*, **46** (3) July 1972, 320 - 338.

The Rise and Fall of Scottish Industry 1707 - 1939, R H Campbell, John Donald Publishers, 1980.

The Springburn Story, J Thomas, David & Charles, 1964 (1974), 260p.

Glasgow Locomotive Builder to the World, M Nicholson, M O'Neill, Polygon Books 1987, 44p.

Dundee's Iron Horses, the story of a lost industry, G MacLennan Steel, Author, 1974, 128p.

The Locomotive Builders of Kilmarnock, R Wear, *Industrial Railway Record* (69) January 1969 325-408.

Locomotive Building in Bristol in the Age of Steam, 1837-1958, P Davis, C E Harvey & J Press, in *Studies in the Business History of Bristol* (109- 136) Ed. C E Harvey & J Press, Bristol Academic Press, 1988.

5. Personal Reminiscences of the British Locomotive Industry

An Apprentice at Hawthorn Leslie & Co Ltd, 1921 - 1925, B Reed, *The Journal of the Stephenson Locomotive Society*, **65** 1989 (735) - (739), 5-12, 46-52, 84-92, 125-133, 165-169.

Reminiscences of a Locomotive Works (Kerr Stuart & Co), L T C Rolt, in *Trains' Sixty Eight* (pp 5-11), Ian Allan Ltd, 1967, 96p.

Locomotive Apprentice at the North British Locomotive Co, N S C Macmillan, Plateway Press, 1992, 80p.

An Apprentice at Robert Stephenson & Hawthorns 1947 - 53, J R Strong *The Journal of the Stephenson Locomotive Society*, May/June 1990, 93-96.

Reminiscences of a Locomotive Engineer, G W McArd, T*he Railway Magazine* (1) March 1959, 161-165 (Kitson & Co) (2) April 1959, 231-235, 238 (NB Loco Co) (3) June 1959, 425-429 (Hunslet Engine Co) (4) July 1959, 494-498 (Armstrong Whitworth & Co).

6. Specialised Locomotives

The Fairlie Locomotive, R A S Abbott, David & Charles, 1970, 103p.

Fireless Locomotives, A C Baker & T D A Civil, The Oakwood Press, 1976, 94p.

Garratt Locomotives of the World, A E Durrant, David & Charles, 1981, 207p.

Kitson Meyer Articulated Locomotives, D Binns, Wyvern Publications, 1985, 128p.

Kitson Meyer Articulated Locomotives, - the definitive history, D Binns, Locomotives International, 1993, 100p.

British-built Mallets, J H Court, *The Railway Magazine*, March 1964, 282-288.

7. Chinese 4-8-4 Locomotives

New 4-8-4 Type Locomotives for the Chinese National Railways, G Collingwood, *The Journal of the Institution of Locomotive Engineers*, **26** (133) September - October 1936, 595-639 .

The Chinese 4-8-4 Locomotives, K Cantlie, *Transactions of the Newcomen Society*, **54**, 1982-83, 127-143.

8. Miscellaneous

(Chapter 5) *Railway Economy: New Art of Transport*, D Lardner, Taylor, Walton & Maberly, 1850, 528p.

The Locomotive Drawing Office, *The Locomotive*, **22**, September 1916, 180-184.

The Standardisation of Locomotives in India, 1910, C Hitchcock, *Proceedings of the Institution of Civil Engineers*, October 1910, 1409-1522.

Locomotive Factory Organisation, *Vulcan Magazine* **2** (2) Summer 1951 - **3** (6) Summer 1955.

Private Locomotive Building and the Indian Connection, C P Atkins in *Bedside Backtrack, Aspects of Britain's Railway History*, Ed. D Jenkinson, (pp 19-24,) Atlantic Transport Publishers, 1993.

Charles Frederick Beyer and his influence, M. Rutherford, *Backtrack*, **12** (11), November 1998, 623-631.

British Locomotive Builders' Plates — A Pictorial Guide, K. Buckle & D Love, Midland Publishing Ltd, 1994, 80p.

9. Repositories of locomotive manufacturers' records

Code

B *Beyer, Peacock* Archive, Museum of Science and Industry in Manchester, Liverpool Road, Manchester, M3 4FB

E HM General Register House, PO Box 36, Edinburgh EH1 3YY

F *Fowler* Archive, The University of Reading, Rural History Centre, Whiteknights, PO Box 229, Reading, RG6 6AG

G The Mitchell Library, North Street, Glasgow, G3 7DN

H *Hawthorn* Archive, Central Library, Prince Georg Square, South Shields, NE33 2PE

L The Leeds Industrial Museum, Canal Road, Leeds LS12 2QF

M Department of Archives, Merseyside Maritime Museum, Albert Dock, Liverpool L3 4AQ

S Sheffield Archives, 52 Shoreham Street, Sheffield, S1 4SP

U Business Records Centre, University of Glasgow Archives, 13 Thurso Street, Dumbarton Road, Glasgow, G12 8QQ

Y Library & Archive, National Railway Museum, Leeman Road, York YO26 4XJ

Y* = copy of document held in NRM Library & Archive

Note

Up to date details concerning access should be obtained by written application. Records may not be fully catalogued or readily accessible for a variety of reasons.